1971

OXFORD LIBRA
AFRICAN LITERA

General Editors

E. E. EVANS-PRITCHARD
G. LIENHARDT
W. H. WHITELEY

Oxford Library of African Literature

════════

A SELECTION OF AFRICAN PROSE
I. Traditional Oral Texts
II. Written Prose
Compiled by W. H. WHITELEY
(*Two volumes*)
(*Not for sale in the U.S.A. or Canada*)

THE HEROIC RECITATIONS OF THE
BAHIMA OF ANKOLE
By H. F. MORRIS

SOMALI POETRY
An Introduction
By B. W. ANDRZEJEWSKI *and* I. M. LEWIS

A SELECTION OF
AFRICAN PROSE

COMPILED BY W. H. WHITELEY

═══

I

TRADITIONAL ORAL TEXTS

OXFORD
AT THE CLARENDON PRESS
1964

Oxford University Press, Amen House, London E.C.4

GLASGOW   NEW YORK   TORONTO   MELBOURNE   WELLINGTON
BOMBAY   CALCUTTA   MADRAS   KARACHI   LAHORE   DACCA
CAPE TOWN   SALISBURY   NAIROBI   IBADAN   ACCRA
KUALA LUMPUR   HONG KONG

PRINTED IN GREAT BRITAIN

PREFACE

By the GENERAL EDITORS

WE approach Africa now as general editors of this library of her literature—unique, we believe, of its kind—with a sense of exhilaration and of urgency: exhilaration because so much unexplored country can be discerned ahead, urgency because in our own short time many compositions recorded only in human memory are being everywhere lost.

If the *Oxford Library of African Literature* draws together and preserves literary works exhibiting something of the variety of the African imagination and its modes of expression, we shall be well satisfied. Perhaps also the interest of others, and not professional scholars only, will be engaged by the many remaining opportunities.

But our intention is not to be misunderstood as the conservation, merely, of archaic conventions or of passing forms of social experience. On the contrary, we think it harmful to African literary studies to divide the past from the present. There is a great need to bring to bear upon African literature the interest in living traditions and the concern for discovering order and proportion within them which Mr. T. S. Eliot, in particular, introduced into European literary criticism with his *Selected Essays*. If we consider any artist without a prejudice in favour of his personal idiosyncrasy—as Eliot observed of poets in the essay 'Tradition and the Individual Talent'—'we shall often find only the best, but the most individual parts of his work may be those in which dead poets, his ancestors, assert their immortality most vigorously'. Chinua Achebe has shown a similar perception in relation to some African writings in his foreword to an early volume in this Library.

A feeling for the whole literature of any single nation, and hence for the context in which its scholars and writers are really working, depends upon the availability of a wide range of texts in the national language or languages. Few African writers today have had access to anything like the full corpus of literature of their own countries, and their interest in it may sometimes have been early diverted by an education based upon European literary models and of these, unfortunately, not always the best. This Library cannot of course hope to assemble a representative collection of works from any single African people; but it may encourage others to collect their own national literatures in a more systematic way than has hitherto usually been attempted. If it does so, it will be by giving an impression of the continental setting to which any African poetry and prose must be referred, and through carefully edited translations into languages common to African and European readers. Through these also, Africa may now make her literary contribution to other continental cultures, as India and Asia have done for many years.

Our first concern in offering these volumes has been the intrinsic interest of any work represented. This is not the time, in our view, to single out a few African 'classics', for no one can pretend to judge of the best until he can judge of enough. The literary interest of a whole continent is not exhausted in a few works of indisputable artistic achievement and, moreover, we are only beginning to discover indigenous African standards of literary value.

The principal aim of this Library is to relate African literature to African life. As the ethnologist, the linguist, the creative writer, and even the traveller collaborate in this task, they may hope to produce fuller and more vivid representations of the cultures of Africa than any one of them could arrive at alone.

E. E. EVANS-PRITCHARD
G. LIENHARDT
W. H. WHITELEY

FOREWORD

Contributed by CHINUA ACHEBE

NOWADAYS new anthologies are always coming out of Africa, but this present work is remarkable both for the great variety of material it has assembled together and for the manner in which Dr. Whiteley has approached his task. It is only too easy to compile an anthology which may do credit to the editor's scholarship, or his industry, or his sense of mission, but which remains lifeless and unreadable. Dr. Whiteley has produced a lively and very readable book. One has the feeling that it was meant to be enjoyed and that the editor has not gone into the field self-consciously trying to salvage bits of the African heritage before an imminent cultural darkness.

The prose tradition of non-literate peoples is often presumed to consist of folk-tales, legends, proverbs, and riddles. Dr. Whiteley reminds us that these categories represent only a part of the tradition. I would go so far as to say that they represent the least important part. If one takes the Igbo society, which I know best, it seems quite clear that the finest examples of prose occur not in those forms but in oratory and even in the art of good conversation. Riddles and proverbs (*inu*) are cast in a rigid mould and cannot be varied at will. Legend (*akuko ani*) and folk-tale (*akuko iro*) are more flexible but only within a certain framework. This more or less rigid form is important because it helps to ensure the survival of these categories of prose. It also makes it possible for a speaker to employ convenient abbreviations. For instance, he might say: 'If an old woman stumbles and falls twice . . .' and leave it at that. His audience would know the rest of the proverb: '. . . the contents of her basket would be numbered.'

Serious conversation and oratory, on the other hand, call for an original and individual talent and at their best belong to a higher order. Unfortunately there is no way of preserving them in a non-literate society. One catches glimpses of the glory of Igbo oratory by listening to the few people remaining in the villages who can deploy the full resources of the language.

This is not in praise of the noble savage. Some of the finest examples of oratory I have heard have been performed from the village pulpit by Christian converts of my father's generation.

The good orator calls to his aid the legends, folk-lore, proverbs, &c., of his people; they are some of the raw material with which he works. Those who wonder why literate Africans take so little interest in collecting their proverbs may not be fully aware that proverbs by themselves have little significance. They are like dormant seeds lying in the dry-season earth, waiting for the rain. In Igbo they serve two important ends. They enable the speaker to give universal status to a special and particular incident and they are used to soften the harshness of words and make them more palatable. They are called in Igbo 'the palm-oil with which words are eaten'. Palm-oil by itself is not food. If you want to eat you must look for yams, plantains, or dried meat; palm-oil and pepper will then be added to them from your wife's hut. If literate Africans cannot be persuaded to be enthusiastic about the collection of proverbs, however, one hopes that African writers will make use of them in dialogue, for which they were originally intended.

The difficulty of translating folk-stories from African languages into English is a very real one, as Dr. Whiteley shows in his own handling of a Tanganyika story, giving us first a barely intelligible word-for-word translation and then a free translation. But despite this basic difficulty all the extracts and stories collected here are easy to read and some are quite beautiful. Every mood is touched on. The sad Hottentot story of girls lured to their death by the song of strange men whose leader is one-eyed reads like an allegory of the tragedy which was soon to overtake the race. 'How Kimyera became king of Uganda', which the indefatigable traveller H. M. Stanley recorded from 'a native lad of Uganda', is a good lusty love-story to which the prim Victorian style in which it is rendered adds a quaint touch of comedy: '. . . . he had been specially attracted by the charms of Wanyana. It was whispered by a few of the more maliciously disposed among the women that a meeting had taken place and that an opportunity had been found by them to inform each other of their mutual passion.' Then, on the lighter side, there is the very funny story of 'The Two Rogues', from Northern Nigeria. Each of the rogues tries to outwit the other and make away with the booty, but always finds that the other is one trick ahead. After many abortive feats of trickery the two decide to be straight with each other, realizing the truth of the Igbo proverb: When a man of tricks dies there is always another man of tricks to bury him.

I found the Cameroon story 'The Englishman and his Pet Animals' remarkable. It reveals the indulgent amusement with which Africans observed the foibles of their European overlords.

'Once upon a time there was an Englishman, and he used to go hunting and shoot game near his home. There came a day that all the game there was finished. So he said, "Now I perceive that all the game animals in my own home forest are finished; so I think I will go and hunt over in Germany."' I would not be surprised if this story was born or given a new dress when Britain took over the Cameroons from the Germans during World War I. In any case it reminds us that the work of creation is not yet finished, that folk-tales, like folk-songs, continue to be born and that new ones take account of all the new things surrounding life today. This syncretism is one of the chief attractions of Amos Tutuola, who is really a folk-writer. Syncretism is, of course, the despair of purists (of those, for instance, who protest when Africans perform traditional dances in shorts instead of raffia skirts which they no longer wear). But any art which seeks to be up to date is at least alive; it has not yet ossified into a museum piece.

Some of the best items in this anthology show this syncretism. The Hausa story 'Adamu and his Beautiful Wife' ends with these words: 'Though Adamu and Sonkowa were now free to live peacefully, he still continued to live with his sincere friends who had helped him throughout his struggle against the intrigues of the leper. He also sent for the parents of his wife and also his own parents. They all came and they lived happily together. He had several sons and daughters, who grew up and helped in raising the standard of education of the country.' If anyone thinks the last sentence is a naïve anticlimax he cannot know much about Africa today.

The second volume of Dr. Whiteley's anthology reflects the new written literature which belongs in time and spirit to the period of Africa's cataclysmic confrontation with Europe. The slave-trade was the most striking feature of the earlier part of this meeting, and it is therefore appropriate that the volume should open with an excerpt from the exciting narrative of the expatriate writer Equiano, a Nigerian slave who obtained his freedom and settled in London.

On the continent itself serious writing did not begin until Africa had had time to learn some European languages. All the writing in the second volume, whether written originally in a European language or not, bears the marks of this learning, and it is not surprising that South and West Africa, which for different reasons progressed farthest in this schooling, have produced most of the writing.

The first writers in West Africa were concerned mostly with religious, political, or racial issues. Their style tended to be heavy with the weight of classical and other erudite allusions, though there were some, like the Hon. J. E. Casely Hayford of the Gold Coast, who wrote pleasantly and elegantly. Many of the more recent writers included in this volume, Camara Laye, Ezekiel Mphahlele, Cyprian Ekwensi, Amos Tutuola, and others, are already well known outside Africa. One of the great merits of this collection is that it has placed such writers at the side of others who because they write in African languages are little known. Men like the late Shaaban Robert, the great Swahili poet, and the veteran Nigerian novelist D. O. Fagunwa, who writes in Yoruba. In comparing passages in this anthology, it was an eye-opener to me to find that Tutuola, for example, came so close to Fagunwa, and I feel certain that every reader will be similarly rewarded by new perceptions of African literary trends and traditions.

CHINUA ACHEBE

ACKNOWLEDGEMENTS

ACKNOWLEDGEMENT is gratefully made to the many people who have collaborated in the compilation of this volume; not only those whose contributions represent samples from their own field-work, but also those who have made special translations from an African original.

In the former category I should like to thank Dr. J. Middleton of University College, London; Professor J. Berry and Dr. B. W. Andrzejewski of the School of Oriental and African Studies, London; Mr. J. S. Mbiti of Westminster College, Cambridge; Professor D. Biebuyck, formerly of Lovanium University, Congo Republic; Dr. J. Jacobs of the University of Ghent, and Mr. Bashir Sambo of Nigeria.

In the latter group I should like to express my thanks to my colleagues at the School of Oriental and African Studies, London: Miss M. M. Green and Mr. W. A. A. Wilson, now in Ghana. Also the late Fr. Cornelius de Goede of Nijmegen, Holland, and Mr. J. W. Court of Kaduna, Nigeria.

Grateful acknowledgement is also made to the following publishers for permission to reproduce material already published:

Routledge & Kegan Paul Ltd. for the texts 'Uthlakanyana' and 'Ukcombekcantsini' from the Rev. Canon Callaway's *Nursery Tales of the Zulus*, Trübner & Co., 1868; also for 'The Little Wise Woman' from *Reynard the Fox, or Hottentot Fables and Tales*, W. H. I. Bleek, Trübner & Co., 1864.

The American Folklore Society for 'How the Older Brother saved the Younger Brother from Death' and 'The Englishman and his Pet Animals' from A. N. Krug's 'Bulu Tales', *Journal of American Folk-lore*, no. 62, 1949; also for 'The Four Uouas' from H. Chatelain's *Folk-Tales of Angola*, 1894.

The Ministry of Education (General Publications), Ibadan, Nigeria, for 'Bambara Knights' by Mallam Amadou Hampate Ba, *Black Orpheus*, November 1959.

The Department of Native Affairs, Pretoria, and N. J. van Warmelo for the extracts from the *History of Matiwane and the Amangwane Tribe*, edited and supplemented by archive documents and other materials by N. J. van Warmelo, Government Printer, Pretoria, 1938; also for the extract from *The Copper Miners of Musina and the Early History of the Zoutpansberg*, edited and supplemented by other material by N. J. van Warmelo, Government Printer, Pretoria, 1940.

Sampson Low, Marston & Co. Ltd. for 'How Kimyera became King of Uganda' from H. M. Stanley's *My Dark Companions and their Strange Stories*, 1893.

The East African Swahili Committee for 'The Arrival of Stanley' from *Maisha ya Hamed bin Muhammed el Murjebi, yaani Tippu Tip*, Supplement to the *East African Swahili Committee's Journal*, nos. 28/2 and 29/1 of 1958–9.

The Chishawasha Mission Press, Salisbury, for permission to reduce 'The Traditional History of the Budya', in translation, which originally appeared in the School Reader, *Citanhatu*.

The Bulletin of the School of Oriental and African Studies and Professor J. Berry for 'The Pineapple Child' originally appearing in vol. xii/2, 1948.

Kongo-Overzee for 'Onecike', originally appearing in *Principes généraux de la nouvelle orthographe otetela-kikusu (Kasai–Kivu)*, vol. xxv, 1959.

I should like also to thank the Editors of *Diogène* for permission to reproduce, in the Introduction, part of my article 'Le Concept de prose littéraire africaine' from no. 37, 1962.

This, and the following volume of Written Prose, were compiled at the initiative of UNESCO, as parts of a comprehensive survey of African literature to be completed in four volumes. The other anthologies in the UNESCO series are 'Selection de textes sacrés d'Afrique Noire', edited by Germaine Dieterlen, 'Chants et poèmes d'Afrique Noire', edited by Paul Mercier, and 'Littérature épique d'Afrique Noire', edited by John Jacobs and Daniel Biebuyck. It is the intention of UNESCO to grant world rights in their anthology as a whole to an American publisher, excluding however, British Commonwealth rights on these two volumes of African prose.

CONTENTS

Contents

states at all, but either loose congeries of largely autonomous groups or wholly autonomous small-scale groups. It seems reasonable to suppose that groups were constantly hiving off from larger ones to form new groups or coming together with other small groups to form larger ones. It is also likely that, except in certain specially favoured areas, subsistence was often difficult, and the pattern of life often threatened by inter-group conflict. The detailed study of such societies has been the concern of anthropologists for the last thirty years,[1] and of historians, also, from more recent times. At the time when European scholars began to take an interest, of a serious and systematic kind, in African societies, some had been in their areas for only a few generations, while others had traditions of unbroken occupation for several centuries. Common to all, however, was their lack of written traditions; one is dealing almost exclusively[2] with an oral tradition, and for parallels in Europe one must look to medieval Ireland and Scotland or to Greece or Jugoslavia in more recent times, though here, written traditions may co-exist.

Within the broad category of oral tradition in particular, it is manifestly unsatisfactory to make the prose/verse distinction turn on a 'non-metrical' element, since a great deal, perhaps most, of African verse—and not only African verse—is non-metrical. A more useful distinction is between what is spoken and what is sung, yet even here one has to recognize that many folk-tales, for example, switch unconcernedly from speech to song and vice versa, and some recognition of hybrid categories is as essential as it is belated. A good example of this is the 'choric speech' of the Zulu (*isigekle*), and similar phenomena have been reported from the Fula of West Africa. It is perhaps preferable that one should regard the prose/verse distinction in terms of points on a single scale of 'patterning', with metrical verse at one end and everyday speech towards the other.

[1] For a general bibliography the standard anthropological textbooks should be consulted, but a useful short bibliography is appended to *Social Anthropology*, E. E. Evans-Pritchard, Cohen & West, 1951. For more detailed studies see *African Political Systems*, M. Fortes and E. E. Evans-Pritchard, O.U.P., 1940; and *Tribes without Rulers*, ed. John Middleton and David Tait, Routledge, 1958.

[2] From such generalization one must, of course, exclude regions such as northern Nigeria, where Arabic was used over large areas and for many centuries, and also the East African coast, where Swahili was written in the Arabic script. For all practical purposes one can discount the scripts which have been recorded from parts of West Africa, e.g. Vai.

INTRODUCTION

FOR a majority of native English speakers a definition of prose as '. . . the ordinary form of written or spoken language without metrical structure' would probably be satisfactory. One would assume it referred to written rather than spoken language, and might implicitly contrast it with a large body of accepted verse, despite the experiments of some modern poets. Again, one may reach a pretty wide measure of agreement as to what constitutes literature, because there is a corpus of material, accumulated over the centuries, which is regarded as such by common consent. Such material provides a basis for judging contemporary work, so that one can make some sort of contrast between 'Gibbon's *History* and tonight's evening paper'. There will always, of course, be argument over certain cases, and views will change with time, but all in all one can expect to find a consensus of opinion on what may be termed the prose literature of English.

The situation in Africa is quite otherwise, and a few words of introduction seem justifiable. Until recent years most of Africa south of the Sahara was occupied by a very large number of disparate societies, speaking languages belonging to several distinct families. Settled agriculture was practised over a wide area; pastoralism was important outside the equatorial forest and the tse-tse belt, and small groups of hunters and food-gatherers occupied areas marginal to both. Some of these societies were large centralized states, which, from time to time, controlled substantial areas of surrounding country and exacted tribute from less powerful neighbours and other states subject to them. As examples one may cite the West African empires of Ghana, Mali, and Songhay; that of Monomotapa in Central Africa, and more recently, the kingdoms around Lake Victoria in Uganda and Ruanda, and the explosive Zulu state under Chaka.[1] On the other hand, many societies were not centralized

[1] For a popular account of African history see *Old Africa Rediscovered*, B. Davidson, 1959: less popular is *Geschichte Afrikas*, D. Westermann, Köln, 1952. For more detailed studies of specific areas see *Ghana: A Historical Interpretation*, J. D. Fage, University of Wisconsin Press, 1959; *Nigerian Perspectives*, Thomas Hodgkin, O.U.P., 1960; *History of East Africa*, vol. i; ed. Roland Oliver and Gervase Mathew, O.U.P., 1963.

However, for the purpose of this introduction, I shall use the distinction between what is spoken and what is sung as my main criterion for setting off prose from verse. Prose will thus include the folk-tale, legend, history, biography, and oratory, together with fixed formulas such as riddles, proverbs, and tongue-twisters. Within the general category of folk-tale one can distinguish animal-stories, tales of supernatural beings or animals (see, for example, Texts 1, 10, 17, 18, 35, 44), and tales in which members of kinship groups are the protagonists (see, for example, Texts 15, 26, 42). Such groupings, it need hardly be said, do not necessarily coincide with those recognized by the people themselves; these groupings being as various as the societies are numerous. Among the Kamba of Kenya, for example, the two main divisions are into stories which are essentially improbable (*mbano*), and stories which contain an element of truth (*ngewa*). Among some societies of the Cameroons, by contrast (P. Alexandre, personal communication), people distinguish between 'mere talk', 'purposeful talk', i.e. oratory, and 'artful talk', i.e. 'prose', the last being rhythmic but not sung.[1] In all the variant types of prose there is a strong didactic element, and the symbiotic relationship between the prose and the society in which it occurs makes it extremely difficult to understand—let alone appreciate—a sample out of context.

One may not be able to accept wholly Sutherland's[2] evolutionary view of the development of prose, so far as Africa

[1] See also the introduction to M. J. and F. S. Herskovits's *Dahomean Narrative*, Routledge & Kegan Paul, 1958, and the discussion in J. Berry's *Spoken Art in West Africa*, L.U.P., 1961. There is an interesting discussion on this in 'Ésotérisme et Fabulation au Soudan', G. Calame-Griaule, *Bulletin d'IFAN*, vol. xvi (Sér. B), 1954.

[2] 'In the history of literature and the history of individual nations, the development of prose is nearly always slower and more uncertain than that of poetry. When we go back to the obscure beginnings of any national literature, what we usually come upon is some kind of poetry; but we may have to wait several centuries before we get prose, and even a longer time before we find it fully articulate, and perhaps longer still before we meet with prose that is a pleasure to read. . . . When prose begins to make its first tentative appearance, it is usually in the form of charters, deeds, proclamations, and practical discourses of one sort or another; and though from the first it may be well or badly written it is hardly likely to be thought of as literature.

'. . . Until a nation has acquired an efficient alphabet, it must depend upon oral transmission; and it is obvious that if what, for want of another word, we must call "literature", depends for its continuing existence on human memories, the outlook for prose is bleak indeed.' *On English Prose*, James R. Sutherland, University of Toronto Press, 1957, pp. 3–4.

is concerned, but it is clear that African societies on the whole possess a far richer verse tradition than that of prose. But they are certainly not unique in this.[1]

To have established a distinction between prose and verse is one thing, to say whether this prose constitutes a literature is quite another.[2] Definitions of literature may be normative or descriptive: the former cites non-controversial examples, the latter attempts to isolate qualities without which the literature is something else, perhaps journalism. One might, for example, define literature with the *Shorter Oxford Dictionary* as '. . . literary productions as a whole, or, less widely, writings esteemed for beauty of form or emotional effect'. The first of these is clearly not helpful in the African context, and the second needs careful elaboration. The problem is a difficult one: what constitutes the distinction between literature and non-literature in societies where the whole continuity of the group is expressed in speech and other actions? Is one to regard the verdict of elders in court-cases as constituting literature, or the strictures of the instructress during the initiation ceremonies? Can one, for example, usefully talk about the literary quality of an initiation text such as that published recently by G. Dieterlen and A. Hampate Ba? (*Koumen*, texte initiatique des Pasteurs Peul, Mouton, 1961.) In a recent stimulating inquiry into the nature of literature, Laurence Lerner[3] has suggested that all theories of literature can be reduced to three:

    (i)   Literature as knowledge.

[1] See, for example, *passim*, H. M. and N. K. Chadwick's monumental *The Growth of Literature*, Cambridge, 1932 (3 vols.).

[2] Divergent views on the status of oral material have been made, explicitly or implicitly, from time to time. The Chadwicks (op. cit.), so far as I can see, never question the literary status of such material, though I have nowhere found any explicit definition of literature. This general view is supported by R. Wellek and A. Warren in their *Theory of Literature*, 1949, '. . . for clearly, any coherent conception [of literature] must include "oral literature" ' (p. 11). On the other hand, the 6th edition (1951) of *Notes and Queries on Anthropology* makes the point that '. . . the repetition of stories, proverbs and traditional sayings may be an integral element of culture, which corresponds among illiterate peoples to literature among the literate' (p. 206), and G. Pfeffer in his 'Prose and poetry of the Ful'be', *Africa*, 1939, maintains that there is literature '. . . only if there is a script, an author to provide material, the possibility of multiplication and distribution and the presence of a public willing to make some sort of reward to the author'.

[3] *The Truest Poetry*, London, 1960. An interesting discussion on this subject also occurs in an article 'Littératures Négro-africaines', P. Alexandre, Encyclopédie 'Clartés', vol. 15, Fasc. 15350, Paris, 1959.

(ii) Literature as the expression of emotion.

(iii) Literature as the arousing of emotion in reader/listener.

These form a useful base from which to discuss the African situation, bearing in mind that the data in this case can be broadly subsumed under the heading of 'traditions', whether these be folk-tales or proverbs, riddles or histories.

If literature is knowledge, then one would expect to find truths, not perhaps necessarily of a scientific variety, but rather of a general and social kind, epitomized by the proverb or allegory. Certainly African societies are rich in such forms. If literature is the expression of emotion then should one accept the view of the Oxfordshire lady who wrote:

> Love made me a poet
> And this I writ
> My heart did do it
> And not my wit[1]

—or should one impose restrictions with Collingwood and deny that literature was the mere arousing of emotion whether for amusement or magic, but rather the result of a complex inter-action between the imagination and the emotion in relation to experience and expressed through language? This raises two important issues: the position of the speaker in society and the subject-matter of the oral material. Both of these require separate treatment below; for the moment we can allow that there should be some expression of emotion, but will return later to the implications of this. If one can imagine literature in which neither of the first two criteria obtained, it is extremely difficult to imagine one which evoked no emotional response in the listener, though equally this is not a sufficient criterion. Many sorts of non-literary utterances evoke emotion in the listener, i.e. a judge giving sentence, teachers bestowing prizes, parents chastizing children: here one is concerned not with direct transmission of news, but rather with the indirect trans-mission, in which the story-teller (court-historian, elder) acts as catalyst of events, presenting not unique events but events as examples of more general phenomena. One might liken the reciter to the distiller, presenting and warming his audience with spirit rather than with ale. The audience, in Africa,

[1] Quoted by Lerner, op. cit., pp. 54–55.

occupies a crucial place: if much of the traditional material serves to reinforce the solidarity and continuity of the group, then the group must clearly be present on occasions when the reciter is the medium between the past and the present.

All Lerner's criteria presuppose the existence of an individual author/reciter and whereas this presents no problem where authorship can be ascertained, the status of the individual in African society, as transmitter and exponent of the oral tradition, is by no means clear. Is traditional material *ipso facto* literature, in which case one can conveniently ignore the individual, or is it the task of the individual to create literature from a mass of traditional material? If one accepts, for example, Pfeffer's evidence[1] that the Ful'be narrator's constant aim was to reproduce the material in the strictest traditional way, then in what light is one to regard such historical traditions? They certainly impart knowledge, and may well both express and arouse emotion, with the individual contribution at a minimum. There will undoubtedly be those who will admit such material to be literature, but I prefer to take the view that if the expression and arousing of emotion is due, not to the individual reciter, but to the material itself, then one still has not got literature but only the stuff from which literature is created. Literature, it seems to me, requires the imposition of individuality of composition or contribution on to the anonymous, but institutionalized, body of tradition. Perhaps, too, there must be a measure of detachment from the 'charter' of society constituted by that tradition.

It must be stressed, however, that the individual does not create in a vacuum; he is always concerned with moulding institutionalized forms of tradition, and the extent to which he is an innovator is evidence of the extent to which he encapsulates that which has gone before.[2] Consider, for example, the recital of folk-tales. The use of the term 'folk-tale' often

---

[1] Pfeffer, op. cit.

[2] In this connexion T. S. Eliot's essay 'Tradition and the individual talent' is illuminating. The essay is reprinted in T. S. Eliot, *Selected Prose*, Penguin Books, 1953. Reference might also be made to J. Middleton Murry, *The Problem of Style*, O.U.P. (Paperback), 1961: '. . . At a certain level of general culture, with certain combinations of economic and social conditions (which it would be well worth while to explore), certain artistic and literary forms impose themselves. These forms the writer is almost impelled to accept, either because he relies on his writing

obscures the fact that in many African societies any given 'folk-tale' is merely one version of a slice from a much larger body of traditional materials, loosely connected by theme or events (see Texts 1, 2). The skill of the individual reciter lies in his handling of certain of these themes, all well known to his audience. Each recital is thus a unique 'literary' event.

Some general consideration must now be given to the position of the individual in relation to the main kinds of prose, though this is a subject which has, as yet, been little considered by investigators.

Where strong centralized kingdoms developed, the accumulation and dissemination of historical traditions was at a premium, and reaches an extreme form in the recognition of the office of court historian, though one may note in passing that these traditions were often in verse rather than prose. Specialization of this kind occurred in various parts of Africa, notably in Ruanda, parts of Uganda and South Africa, but no study of the role of such individuals has yet been made. We do not know to what extent such individuals were innovators or merely recorders, though if we can draw any inferences from our own society we might suppose that events were shaped according to the views of the current authority, rather than to those of an individual artist[1] (see Texts 4–6, 11–13, 20, 21, 23.) In the field of folk-tales, legends, proverbs, and riddles, which comprise the bulk of the prose tradition, the greater part of the material was probably accessible to most adult members of the group, since it constituted a fundamental part of an individual's heritage, distinguishing him or her from others in similar groups elsewhere, and indeed reinforcing the identity of the group as a whole. There was thus every incentive for an individual to acquire a comprehensive stock of his group's traditional prose, but little incentive for the emergence of individual reciters specializing in the recital of such material. The Kamba of

for his living, or because he feels instinctively that he must embrace the means necessary to reaching the largest possible audience'.

[1] Notice the injunction to field-workers in the 5th edition (1929) of *Notes and Queries on Anthropology*, to observe '. . . whether there is any body of men whose duty it is to transmit traditions uncorrupted—though even this does not preclude deliberate alteration of them from motives of piety, vanity or self-interest . . .'. There is an interesting discussion of this point in Jan Vansina's stimulating *De la Tradition Orale*, Tervuren, 1961 (esp. pp. 92–97, 102–10).

Kenya are perhaps typical of this: there would usually be someone in each homestead who told traditional stories to members
of the household, but it is in the songs rather than in the stories
that individual talents are encouraged and professional Kamba
singers are well known throughout Kenya. This seems to be a
characteristic pattern in many African societies, though there
are some, of which I have personal knowledge, where especially
skilled raconteurs are still in demand. Among the Yao of
southern Tanganyika, for example, there are still a few professional reciters, both men and women, though they have
ceased to accept pupils for training as they did formerly. Their
handling of the traditional stories—interspersed with songs—is
followed attentively and critical discussion takes place after
each recital. In fact, however, we have quite inadequate knowledge of the contributions made by individuals to the body of
traditions generally, and of the qualities which people thought
were praiseworthy in the performances of such raconteurs.
Though educated Africans have, as yet, contributed little to our
understanding of the situation, it is to them that one now looks
for elucidation and guidance.

   In deploring our lack of information on the part played by
the individual, one must remember two things: firstly, the very
fact of committing prose traditions to writing robs them of much
of their individuality: no written account, however conscien-
tious—and very many of them were far from this—can possibly
reproduce the verbal nuance, the delicate allusion, or the voice
quality of the original. This is a point which has been made by
various authors at different times during the last hundred years,
though with little effect. The first edition of *Notes and Queries on
Anthropology* (1874) stresses that '. . . it is desirable to take them
[stories] down verbatim from the lips of a skilled story-teller,
as they thus form specimens of the language in its best form,
exhibiting native metaphor, wit and picturesque diction . . .'.
A point similar to this was made some years later by Chatelain[1]
when deploring the poor qualities of folk-lore collections to
date. He complains that '. . . the essential qualities of folk-lore,
those embodied in words, have been ignored, and the moral and
intellectual world of Africa is, today, as much a *terra incognita* as
geographical Africa was fifty years ago'. More recently the

---

[1] *Folk Tales of Angola*, Amer. Folklore Soc., 1894.

point has been forcefully made by P. Itayemi and P. Gurrey in
the Introduction to their collection of *Folk Tales and Fables*
(Penguin Books, 1952) from West Africa. '. . . Folk tales, of
course, should be told in their vernacular idiom. Told in these
translations, they lose two important things: they lose many of
the jokes and the puns, and the funny twists of language that the
listeners originally enjoyed, and waited eagerly for when the
well-known story was begun. They lose, too, the special songs
that are so often part of them, especially those of the Yoruba.'[1]
Secondly, the predominant interest of those who collected such
material for our library shelves was in the content rather than
in the style of the piece. Explorers and missionaries of the
nineteenth century saw African societies in evolutionary terms,
as representing stages through which other more complex
societies had passed. They were, therefore, interested mainly in
the content of African tradition, they looked for motifs, symbols,
and personalities, and compared them with examples from
other parts of the world.[2] This was a fertile period not only for
comparative folk-lore in particular, but for comparative studies
generally, as testified by the work of such scholars as Frazer,
Schmidt, and Wundt.

On the other hand, the difficulties facing these early field-
workers were formidable: the mere task of learning the languages and reducing them to writing was to occupy many years,
and there are still a majority of languages for which no adequate
description is available. One has to remember also, that the
main purpose of such studies was to make the Christian message
accessible to pagan peoples, not to evaluate an African literature. Our debt, therefore, to missionary-linguists is great: men
like Krapf and Steere in East Africa; Callaway in South

---

[1] For further discussion of this point see J. Berry, op. cit. It seems that students of
oral literature in other parts of the world may have paid greater attention to the
role of the individual than has been the case in Africa. See, for example, 'Folklore
in the Soviet Union', Margaret Schlauch, *Science and Society*, vol. viii/3, 1944, and
the extremely stimulating account of Jugoslav oral literature in Albert B. Lord's
The Singer of Tales, Harvard University Press, 1960.

[2] See, for example, Alice Werner's study of African mythology in *The Mythology
of All Races*: 'Africa', vol. vii, Archaeological Society of America, 1925. Individual
collections of texts commonly included comparative notes. See, for example,
Nursery Tales of the Zulus, Rev. Canon Callaway, Trübner & Co., 1868; *Reynard
the Fox in South Africa: or Hottentot Fables and Tales*, W. H. I. Bleek, Trübner & Co.,
1864; *Kamba Folk-lore: II. Tales of Supernatural Beings and Adventures*, G. Lindblom,
Uppsala, 1935.

Africa; Chatelain in Angola; and Bentley and Christaller in West Africa compiled collections some of which have not yet been bettered. Equally it would be wrong to imagine that it was only the missionaries who were solely interested in the content of traditional prose: anthropologists who collected texts did so for their anthropological value, and as Doke has pointed out '. . . the mere recording of ethnographic, historical or technological texts need not *ipso facto* contribute much to the literature of a people'.[1] Even in very recent times, for example, anthropological interest in historical texts has been directed solely at the historical value, a fact which is stated not so much in criticism as in observation.[2] Following on the period of initial activity at the turn of the century, the collection of traditional material lapsed: social anthropologists concentrating on institutional, synchronic studies of individual societies; linguists on structural or grammatical studies; and missionaries on pastoral work. In the years since 1920 the amount of material collected has been extremely small, and it is not until recent times that the development of the tape-recorder has made possible a quality of reproduction undreamed of by earlier workers, and also made possible the collection of quantities of material in relatively short periods.[3]

Where such recordings are available one can readily appreciate something of the qualities contributed to the recital of traditional material by the individual, and if we have not yet solved the problem of transferring these qualities to paper, at least the problem can be stated.

The following selection of texts, together with its companion

[1] 'Lamba literature', C. M. Doke, *Africa*, iv, 1934.

[2] For example: 'A Lunda love story and its consequences': selected texts from traditions collected by Henrique Dias de Carvalho at the court of Mwatianvwa in 1887. Translated and annotated by V. W. Turner, *Rhodes-Livingstone Journal*, vol. xix, Manchester, 1955; 'Kazembe's charter': extract from *Ifikolwe Fyandi na Bantu bandi, Mwata Kazembe XIV*, Macmillan, 1951; I. Cunnison, *Northern Rhodesia Journal*, vol. iii/3, 1957. Also, the recently started series of Central Bantu Historical Texts, Rhodes-Livingstone Institute, Lusaka.

[3] A good example of this is furnished by some recent American work; thus: 'While in West Africa on a Fulbright award, I recorded among the Yoruba approximately a thousand folktales, three thousand songs, between seven and eight hundred riddles, numerous philosophical sayings, and some other varieties of their folklore.' From 'The Role of Folklore in the life of the Yoruba of Southwestern Nigeria', L. Turner, *Report of the Ninth Annual Round Table Meeting on Linguistics and Language Study* (1958), Georgetown, 1960.

selection of written texts, was originally sponsored by
U.N.E.S.C.O., who also provided funds for its compilation.[1]
Since it was their wish that volumes in this project should be
unilingual, I have restricted my choice to those texts which have
been or could be translated directly from a local African language into English. There are only two groups of texts where this
is not strictly so: in one (9–10) the English version was prepared
in collaboration with a French/Tetela speaker, and in the other
(12–13) the translator was himself conversant with English/
French and Luba. This has meant, of course, that I have had,
regretfully, to exclude the work of continental scholars whose
translation into a metropolitan language such as French,
German, Dutch, or Italian could not be referred back to the
original language for direct translation into English. There are
those who believe that translation from one metropolitan language to another is justifiable, even where presenting texts of a
literary nature,[2] but it is one I cannot share. We ought to be
concerned, not with eliciting 'themes' nor with getting 'the
general feel' of a text, but with the literary quality of texts. It is
rare enough to find English translations of French or German
literature which both convey the spirit of the original and stand
in their own right as literature. How much more difficult to find
such translations from the African field where translators were
often not concerned with the literary aspect of the tradition at
all—nor even, perhaps, aware that such existed. Under those
conditions retranslation is out of the question.

Those who compile anthologies are often embarrassed by a
plethora of suitable material; once again the African field provides an exception, not because material does not exist, but
because what is available often lacks one requirement or another. For example, I cannot share the claim of a recent com-
piler of an anthology of Japanese literature[3] to have restricted
the choice of texts to those which translate into 'enjoyable

---

[1] There have been several previous anthologies of African literature: for example,
the *Anthologie Nègre*, B. Cendrars, Paris, 1921 (tr. into English by M. Bianco under
the title *The African Saga*, New York, 1927); *Darkness and Light*, ed. P. Rutherfoord,
Faith Press, Johannesburg, 1959 (reprinted as *African Voices*, Vanguard Press, New
York, 1959); *An African Treasury*, selected by Langston Hughes, Gollancz, 1961.
The last two are primarily concerned with modern writing.

[2] See, for example, M. J. and F. S. Herskovits, op. cit.

[3] *Anthology of Japanese Literature*, compiled and edited by Donald Keene, George
Allen & Unwin, 1956.

English'. Too often the available translations are in archaic, bizarre, or literal English, read as curiosities rather than as literature. While this in itself may be a matter for regret, the fact that a story is written in good English is certainly no guarantee of its being also a good example of African prose; perhaps rather the contrary. A more serious inadequacy in the material is the fact that it is primarily *elicited* material, collected without concern for the literary form of the text or for the context in which it was recited. One does not, of course, minimize the difficulties of collecting texts, especially in the days before the transistorized tape-recorder, but the resultant picture of the oral prose is, at best, inadequate. Finally, the nature of the symbolism that occurs, the strictly localized nature of events described, and the close link between society and text, make any of these texts difficult to follow without some form of contextualization. Yet one is reluctant to overburden the text with a copious battery of notes which take the eye from the page and the attention from the narrative.[1] I suggest, therefore, that those whose interest is quickened from a reading of the extracts might usefully consult the African Bibliography series being prepared by the International African Institute, or the extremely useful series of studies in this Institute's Ethnographic Survey of Africa.

What I have tried to do in the following pages is to present a representative selection from the oral tradition, representative both from a geographical point of view and from that of genre. I have, however, deliberately minimized the selection of animal stories, since there are a large number already in print. I have also omitted any selection of proverbs, riddles, or tongue-twisters, not only because they merit separate treatment in detail but because, even more than other kinds of prose, they need to be cited in context. Proverbs, in any case, have been exceptionally fortunate in the treatment they have received, from Christaller in the last century to Hulstaert in this.

The difficulties of achieving my objective have been considerable, and I do not claim to have overcome them, but if a reading of this selection stimulates a critical interest in oral prose and a reappraisal of its literary status, it will have amply justified its compilation.

[1] But see the interesting analysis of Thomas O. Beidelman in ' "Hyena and Rabbit": a Kaguru representation of matrilineal relations', *Africa*, xxxi, 1961.

SOUTH AFRICA

1

Uthlakanyana

From *Nursery Tales and Traditions of the Zulus*, Rev. Canon Callaway, Trübner, 1868.

The Zulu of Natal are one of the most important members of the
Nguni-speaking group of peoples, numbering rather more than two
million. They became famous during the early part of the nineteenth
century under their powerful king and military leader Chaka (see
vol. ii, Text 5). Though they possess a rich prose literature, this has
been rather overshadowed by the remarkable development of praise-
songs, *izibongo*, and other forms of verse.

This particular story is extremely long; one might, indeed, say
that it was not one story, but a whole cycle of stories with a central
character. Only a portion of it can, therefore, be included here.

Extract from the Preface to this tale:

UTHLAKANYANA is a very cunning man; he is also very small,
of the size of a weasel. This man was despised constantly among
those people, whom he used to deceive, and from whom he
sprang; for they thought they could not be deceived by a child
—they could be deceived by a man as big as themselves. Therefore, through not understanding him, that he had not grown
because he was overweighted by cunning and wisdom, and
so was undersized, and became a contemptible dwarf, they
habitually despised him at all times. But he deceived a man,
through his not being clearly seen to be, in fact, the very man to
deceive. He was called also Ukcaijana-bogconono, Mathlab'-
in-doda-i-s'-emi. The word Ukcaijana signifies a little red
animal, which has a black-tipped tail. And this animal is cleverer
than all others, for its cunning is great. If a trap is set for a wild
cat, it comes immediately to the trap, and takes away the mouse
which is placed there for the cat: it takes it out first; and when
the cat comes, the mouse has been already eaten by the weasel.

[*The preface continues:*]

(Uthlakanyana speaks before he is born.)

A certain woman happened to be pregnant. When her time was fully come, the child spoke in the womb, and said, 'Mother, give birth to me at once; the cattle of my father are devoured by the people.' The mother said, 'Just come and listen. Here is a prodigy. The child is speaking within me.' They asked, 'What does he say?' 'He tells me to give birth to him at once; he says the cattle in the kraal are coming to an end.'

(The father calls the people together.)

The father had slaughtered some oxen. The people came together, and left the cattle-kraal with the men, crying, 'Come and hear. Here is a prodigy, an unborn child speaking!' The father said, 'Let the child speak according to your saying.' The child spoke, and said, 'Yes, indeed, I say, let my mother give birth to me; for the cattle in the kraal are coming to an end. And, I say, let me go and get ready flesh for myself.' The people wondered, and said, 'What is going to happen?'

(All the people are put out of the hut and Uthlakanyana is born.)

The father said, 'Let all go out of the house. Do you give birth to him, that we may see if it is a man or not. It is a prodigy, this.' All went out. The father said, 'Let no man remain. But all go out, because he began to speak when his mother was alone.' So they went out: and the child was born. As soon as he was born, he stood up. His mother said, 'Come here, and let me cut off that which is hanging from you.' The child said, 'No, indeed. Don't you cut me; I am going to cut myself. I too am old. I am a man of the council.' He took his father's spear, and cut himself, and threw it down. His mother took water, and washed him.

(Uthlakanyana goes out, and the people run away.)

He went out with the spear; his mother took it from him outside: he left it, and went into the cattle-kraal. The men ran away. He sat down by the fire, and ate a strip of meat, which the men had been eating. The men came back, and said, 'So then it is a man! an old man! We thought it was a child.' The men inquired, and said, 'Is this the very child which was speaking within you?' The mother said, 'It is he.'

(The men praise his wisdom, and propose that he shall be the great child.)

They said, 'O, we thank you, our queen. You have brought forth for us a child who is wise as soon as he is born. We never saw a child like this child. This child is fit to be the great child among all the king's children, for he has made us wonder by his wisdom.'

(Uthlakanyana proposes a test of manhood.)

'Yes, indeed', said the child. 'Father, since you say I am a child (I perceive that you, for your part, think I am a child), take a leg of beef, and throw it below the kraal, that we may see who will get it first. Let all your people, both boys and men, and me, go to fetch the leg, so at length we shall see who is the man. He shall be the man who gets the leg.' So the father took the leg, and threw it below the kraal. They all crowded together at the opening, at the upper part of the kraal; but he went out at the lower, creeping through the enclosure; and met them when he was already returning with the leg. He said, 'Mother, just take it. Here is my meat.' His mother said, 'I am glad this day, because I have given birth to a wise man.'

(Uthlakanyana practises hypocrisy, and appropriates the property of other people.)

He returned to the cattle-kraal. His father was giving another man some meat. He said, 'Hand it to me, that I may put it for you in your house.' The man replied, 'Yes, certainly, child of the king.' He took the meat, and went into the house; he took down the eating mat and stick, and smeared blood on them, and went out with the meat, and took it to his mother, and said, 'Mother, take it; here is my meat.' He gave thanks to each of the men (as he took the meat from him); and gave thanks again on his return. Again, he did the same to another man; he took his meat in the same way; he said, 'Hand it to me, that I may put it for you in your house.' He did with that as he had done with the first; he smeared the feeding mat and stick; he left them in the same way, and took the meat to his own house, and said, 'Mother, take it; here is my meat.' His mother thanked him, and said, 'I have given birth to a man this day.' In the whole company there was not one who found his meat. The whole of it was in the house of the boy, who was born on the day the oxen of his father were slaughtered. The sun set. All the people of the village inquired of him when they did not find the meat. He said, 'Look at the stick and the feeding-mat, whether I did not place it on the mat, and take down the stick and hang it up, as meat is hung up?' They said, 'Yes, we see the feeding-mat is bloody, and the stick is bloody. Then has the meat been taken down?' So he said, '(Yes), for there is the mat really bloody.' All made the same inquiry; and he answered them all alike. He persisted in making the feeding-mat a witness to all the people of his father's village.

(The women express great doubt as to Uthlakanyana being a real man.)

The women of the kraal cried out saying, 'What is this that has been born today? What sort of a man is this that has been born? We never saw the like. Why did you send him, since you clearly see that this is Uthlakanyana? Do you say he is a man? Do you say there ever was such a man, who knew how to speak thus whilst a child; and who was so strong that he could get the better of old men? Did you not see him when he took the leg of beef? You might then have understood that this man was not produced in a natural way. He got into the queen; he got in; he was not produced in a natural way; and as for the king, he is not his son. All we women deny it now; and you men will see it some other day. He will do great things, for he spoke before he was born. There, he has taken away your meat from you by his mouth, and you all old men too; and he circumvented even his father about his leg of beef. He will do prodigies; for he, too, is a prodigy, a real prodigy.'

Thus, all that meat was finished.

2

Ukcombekcantsini

From the same source: this also is an exceptionally long story
and only part of it is given here.

(The wives of a certain king give birth to crows. His queen has no child.)

THERE was a certain king of a certain country; he used to have children who were crows, he had not one child that was a

human being; in all his houses his children were crows. But his
queen had no child; it was said she was barren; she remained
a long time without having any child. All used to jeer her, and
even the very women who gave birth to crows, saying, 'We indeed do give birth only to crows; but you give birth to nothing.
Of what use then do you say you are?' She cried, saying, 'But
did I make myself? For even you are mothers, because it was
said, "Be ye mothers".'

(The childless queen receives assistance from some pigeons.)

At length she went to dig; when she was digging, and the
garden was now nearly finished, two pigeons came to her as she
was sitting on the ground and weeping. One said to the other,
'Vukutu.' The other said, 'Why do you say "Vukutu" and not
ask why she is crying?' She said, 'I am crying because I have no
child. The other wives of the king give birth to crows; but I give
birth to nothing.' One said, 'Vukutu.' The other said, 'Why do
you say "Vukutu" and not ask her what she will give us, if we
give her power to have a child?' She replied, 'I could give all I
possess.' One said, 'Vukutu.' The other said, 'Why do you say
"Vukutu" and not ask what food she will give us?' She said,
'I would give you my amabele.' One said, 'Vukutu.' The other
said, 'Why do you say "Vukutu," since we do not eat amabele?'
She said, 'I will give you amadumbi.' One said, 'Vukutu.' The
other said, 'Why do you say "Vukutu," and do not tell her we
do not like amadumbi?' She mentioned all the kinds of foods she
had. They refused it all. At length she said, 'That is all the food
I have.' The pigeon said, 'Vukutu: you have amabele; but for
our part we like castor-oil seeds.' She said, 'O, I have castor-oil
seeds, sir.' One said, 'Vukutu.' The other said, 'Why do you say
"Vukutu," and not tell her to make haste home at once, and
fetch the castor-oil seeds?'

(The queen fetches castor-oil seeds for the pigeons.)

The woman ran home at once; on her arrival she took the
castor-oil seeds which were in a pot, and poured them into a
basket, placed them on her head, and went with them to the
garden. On her arrival one said, 'Vukutu.' The other said, 'Why
do you say "Vukutu," and not tell her to pour the seeds on the
ground?' She poured the castor-oil seeds on the ground. The
pigeons picked them all up.

(The pigeons draw blood from her, and tell her what to do with the clot.)

When they had eaten them all, one said, 'Vukutu.' The other said, 'Why do you say "Vukutu," and not ask her if she has brought a horn and a lancet?' She said, 'No.' One said, 'Vukutu.' The other said, 'Why do you say "Vukutu," and not tell her to go and fetch a horn and a lancet?' She ran home, and fetched a horn and a lancet, and came back immediately. On her arrival one said, 'Vukutu.' The other said, 'Why do you say "Vukutu," and not tell her to turn her back to us?' She turned her back to them. One said 'Vukutu.' The other said, 'Why do you say "Vukutu," and not scarify her on the loins?' The pigeon cupped her; but when he had finished cupping her, he took the horn, and poured the clotted blood into it. One said, 'Vukutu.' The other said, 'Why do you say "Vukutu," and not tell her on reaching home to find a large vessel, and pour the clotted blood into it, until two moons die; and then uncover the vessel?' She went home and did so.

(She finds two children in the clot at the end of four months.)

She remained two months: when the third new moon appeared, she found two children; she took them out of the vessel; and placed them again in another large pot. She remained three moons without looking into it. When she looked on the fourth moon, she found them now large, and laughing. She greatly rejoiced.

(She conceals the children, and feeds them by night.)

She went to dig. And when she reached the garden, she sat down till the sun went down, saying, 'Can it be that my children can live? For I am jeered by the other women; and even they, forsooth, do not give birth to human beings; they give birth to crows.' In the afternoon she would return home. When it was evening, and she was about to lie down, she shut up the doorway with the wicker door, and with a mat, saying, 'Then, although anyone pass by the door, he will see nothing.' She waited, and when she saw that the people no longer went up and down in the village, she took her children, and placed them on a mat, and took milk and gave them; the boy drank it, but the little girl refused it. When she had remained with them a long time, she put them back again into their place; and slept.

(The crows trouble the queen.)

As regards their growth, both grew very fast; at length they crawled on the ground, not having been seen by anyone; at length they walked, their mother concealing them from the people. They remained in the house, not going out, their mother not allowing them, saying, if they went out they would be seen by the crows, and they would kill them; for they used to vex her in her very house. For it was so that when she had risen in the morning, and fetched water and then went out to dig, when she returned in the afternoon, she found the water spilt over the whole house, and the ashes taken out of the fireplace, and the whole house white with the ashes. She said, 'This is done to me because I do not give birth even to these crows; for if I too gave birth, I should not be treated thus; for I have now been afflicted for a long time in this way; and even with my husband who married me it is the same; he no longer regards me as a human being, because I have no child.'

(The queen gives the girl a name.)

Both grew until they were great children; the little girl was at length a grown-up maiden, and the boy a young man. The mother said to them, 'Since you are now so big, my children, but have no name—'; she said to the girl, 'As for you, your name is Ukcombekcantsini.' The boy said, 'For my part, do not give me a name; for I too will receive my name of manhood, when I have grown up, from my father; I do not wish to have a name now.' So the mother agreed.

(The boy and girl go out when their mother is absent, and make some acquaintances.)

It happened at noon when the mother was not there, the girl said, 'Let us go and fetch water, since the crows have spilt the water of our mother.' The boy said, 'Did not mother forbid us to go outside?' The girl said, 'By whom shall we be seen, since all the people have gone to dig?' The boy agreed. The girl took a water-vessel; she went to the river, both going together. But as for the boy, his peculiarity was that he was white; but the girl was very shining. So they went, and reached the river, and dipped water. When she had filled the vessel, she said to the boy, 'Put it on my head.' When he was just about to put it on her head, they saw a line of many people coming to them.

When they came to the river, they said, 'Give us to drink.' He dipped water with a cup, and gave the first. The second asked also, saying, 'Give me to drink.' He gave him to drink. All asked in like manner, until he had given them all to drink.

(They tell their new acquaintances something about themselves, and learn something about their acquaintances.)

They said, 'To what village do you belong?' They replied, 'To that one on the hill.' They said, 'Is there anyone at home?' They said, 'No, there is no one.' They said, 'To which house do you belong?' They said, 'To that which is last near the main entrance.' They said, 'Which is the queen?' They replied, 'The queen was our own mother; but it happened that, because she had no child, her house was removed, and placed near the entrance.' The children inquired of them, 'And you, to what nation do you belong?' They replied, 'We came from yonder. We are looking for a very beautiful damsel; for the king of our nation is going to be married.' They said, 'Is he then about to take his first wife?' They assented. They asked, 'Of what nation are you?' They said, 'We are Abahhwebu.' The girl said, 'And the king of your nation, is he an Umhhwebu?' They replied, 'No; he is not of the same race as ourselves; we only are Abahhwebu. And we are not many; we are but one troop.' So the Abahhwebu departed.

(The queen is displeased.)

The boy put the water-vessel on her head. They went up the hill to their home, and sat down. In the afternoon when the mother returned from digging, she asked, 'By whom was this water fetched?' They said, 'By us.' She said, 'Did I not forbid you to go outside? By whom, then, were you told to go and fetch water?' The boy said, 'I refused for my part, but Ukcombekcantsini said, "Let us go and fetch water".' The mother said, 'Did no man see you?' They replied, 'We were seen by some Abahhwebu, who formed a very long line. They asked us whose children we were; we said we belonged to this village.' They were then silent. They remained for many days. But they were unknown to anyone of their own village; they were known by the Abahhwebu only.

(A large company come to the royal kraal, with cattle, to ask the king's daughter in marriage.)

It came to pass on another occasion there came very many cattle in the afternoon with very many people. All the people of the village said, 'It is an army; into what place has it made a foray, and taken so many cattle as these?' They saw many men coming to their village; they left many of the cattle outside; they entered with others into the very village. On their arrival they drove them into the cattle-pen, and went to the upper part, and stood there and respectfully asked his daughter from the father. All the people of the village were silent, being silent from wonder, saying, 'Is there a man who could come and select from among crows one to be his bride? For there is not a girl who is a human being in this village.' But the men asked as though they knew the damsel. At length the women said, 'If you are come to select a bride, which is the damsel among all these of ours? That mother will be glad whose daughter shall be selected with so many cattle as these.'

(The mothers of the crows jeer the queen.)

All the women went out of the houses and stood outside; some ran to the entrance, saying, 'Ye, ye! is the woman who has no child satisfied as to whose are these bridegroom's men?' saying thus for the purpose of jeering the childless one, for they did not know that it was she who really had a girl; for they had given birth to crows only. The men went out in anger together with the father of the crows, he being in a rage with the women, and saying, 'Away with you; away with you! For which girls of yours do you make this huzzahing? since you have given birth only to crows. Who would cast away so many cattle as these for a crow's dowry?' The men said, 'Make haste into your houses, and cease this noise.'

(The king tells them he has no daughter; but they persist in asking his daughter in marriage.)

The owner of the village went to the bridegroom's men, and said, 'As for me I have no girl. I am the father of mere crows, and of nothing else. Take your cattle, and go home with them to your people.' They replied, 'We beseech thee not to refuse us; for we know that there is a damsel at this place which is a human being.' The head of the village swore solemnly that there was no damsel at his home. At length the bridegroom's people looked at each other, being desirous of inquiring of the Abahhwebu who had come there at first; they asked them, 'Did you in truth see a damsel at this place?' The Abahhwebu replied, 'We did see one at this place: we can point out the house into which she entered.' They inquired which it was. They said, 'It is that which is the last but one.' They said, 'O chief of this village, we are indeed acquainted with your daughter; we can even point out the house in which she is.' The chief of the village replied, speaking in anger, 'Are these men then truly so very wise? For I the father of the children tell you, there is not a girl in this place that is a human being. But you dispute the matter with me, because you have come to laugh at me, because I am not a father of human beings. That house to which you point, the occupier of it has not given birth to so much as a crow.'

3

The Little Wise Woman

From *Reynard the Fox in South Africa, or Hottentot Fables and Tales*, W. H. I. Bleek, Trübner, 1864.

The Hottentot peoples live scattered over South Africa and especially in South-West Africa: there are probably not more than a 100,000 of them.

A GIRL, it is said, went to seek for onions. As she arrived at the place where they grew, she met with some men, one of whom was blind (i.e. half-blind, having only one eye). As she dug (for the onions) the men helped her, digging also. When her sack was full, they said to her, 'Go, tell the other girls, that many of you may come.' So she went home and told her companions, and early the next morning they started. But a little girl followed them. The other girls said, 'Let the little girl go back.' But her elder sister protested against this, saying, 'She runs by herself, you need not put her into your *awa*-skin.'

So they went all together, and having reached the onion-ground, began to dig. Now the little girl saw traces of feet, and said to the one who had guided them thither, 'Wonderful! Whence so many traces? Were you not alone here?' The other replied, 'I walked about and looked out; therefore they must of course be many.' The child, however, did not believe that if the other girl had been alone the traces could be so many, and felt uneasy; for she was a wise little woman. From time to time she rose (from her work) and peeped about, and once, while doing this, found by chance an ant-eater's hole. Still further spying about, she perceived some men, but they did not see her. She then returned and continued digging with the other girls, without, however, saying anything. But in the midst of their work she always rose and looked about her. So the others asked her, 'Why do you always spy about you, and leave off digging? What a girl!' But she continued her work in silence. When she rose from it again, she saw the men approaching. As they drew near, the One-eyed blew through a reed pipe the following air:

'Today there shall blood flow, blood flow, blood flow!'

The little girl understood what was blown on the reed. She said to the elder ones, whilst they were dancing, 'Do you also understand the tune that is blown on the reed?' But they only said, 'What a child she is!' So she mixed in the dance with the others; but managed while so doing to tie her sister's caross-cloak to her own, and in this manner they danced on, till it became very noisy, and then they found an opportunity to slip away.

On their way out the little sister asked, 'Do you understand the reed? I mean what is blown on it?' She answered, 'I do not understand it.' Then the little girl explained to her that the tune on the reed said, 'Today blood shall flow!' When they walked along, the little girl let her elder sister go first, and herself followed, walking backwards, and carefully stepping in her sister's traces, so that they thus left only one set of footmarks, and these going in a contrary direction. In this manner they arrived at the ant-eater's hole.

But the men killed all those girls who had remained dancing with them. When the eldest of those who had escaped heard their wailing, she said, 'Alas, my sisters!' But the younger one answered her, 'Do you think you would have lived if you had remained there?'

Now 'One-eye' was the first to miss the sisters, and said to the other men, 'Where may the two handsome girls be who danced with me?' The others replied, 'He lies. He has seen with his eye' (satirically meaning he had seen wrongly). But 'One-eye' insisted that 'two girls were truly missing'. Then they went to find their spoor, but the traces had been rendered indistinct enough to puzzle them.

When the men arrived at the ant-eater's hole, they could not see that the footmarks went farther, so they spied into the hole, but saw nothing. Then 'One-eye' looked also, and he saw the girls, and cried, 'There they sit.' The others now looked again, but still saw nothing; for the girls had covered themselves with cobwebs.

One of the men then took an assegai, and piercing through the upper part of the hole, hit the heel of the larger girl. But the little wise woman took hold of the assegai, and wiped off the blood. The elder sister was about to cry, but the little one warned her not to.

When 'One-eye' spied again, the little girl made big eyes at him. He said, 'There she sits.' The others looked too, but as they could see nothing they said (satirically), 'He has only seen with his eye.'

At last the men got thirsty, and said to 'One-eye', 'Stay you here, and let us go to drink, and when we have returned you may go also.'

When 'One-eye' was left alone there, the little girl said (conjuring him):

> 'You dirty son of your father,
>> Are you there? Are you alone not thirsty?
> Oh, you dirty child of your father!
>> Dirty child of your father!'

'I am indeed thirsty,' said 'One-eye', and went away.

Then the two girls came out of the hole, and the younger one took her elder sister on her back, and walked on. As they were going over the bare, treeless plain, the men saw them, and said, 'There they are, far off', and ran after them.

When they came near, the two girls turned themselves into thorn trees, called 'Wait-a-bit', and the beads which they wore became gum on the trees. The men then ate of the gum and fell asleep. Whilst they slept, the girls smeared gum over the men's eyes and went away, leaving them lying in the sun.

The girls were already near their kraal, when 'One-eye' awoke, and said:

> 'Oh, the disgrace! fie on thee!
> Our eyes are smeared over; fie on thee, my brother!'

Then they removed the gum from their eyes, and hunted after the girls; but the latter reached home in safety, and told their parents what had happened.

Then all lamented greatly, but they remained quietly at home, and did not search for the other girls.

4

Matiwane and the White Men

From the *History of Matiwane and the Amangwane Tribe*, edited (and supplemented by archive documents and other material) by N. J. van Warmelo, Government Printer, Pretoria, 1938, ch. 5.

The AmaNgwane are a Zulu-speaking tribe of Natal numbering about 30,000 (1938). About 1800 they were living in northern Natal and in 1818 were attacked by Chaka, and moved over the Drakensberg range, and in their turn attacked the southern Sotho. They continued to live by plunder under their chief Matiwane. In 1828, while Chaka was attacking the Pondo, the AmaNgwane recommenced raiding into the country of the Thembu, across the Orange River, and the Government, fearing an influx of refugees, dispatched a force under Lt.-Col. Somerset, who routed the AmaNgwane at the battle of Mbholompo on 28 February 1828.

This extract is from the history of the tribe as recounted by Msebenzi, the son of Matiwane's second son Macingwane, when on a visit to his brother's son, the Rev. Albert Hlongwane. It is therefore an example of elicited history, rather than an example from a spontaneous recital, though it seems likely that it is a fairly good example of its kind.

(Matiwane encounters first white men.)

So a commando was armed for war, a party of those English that rode on saddles with horns. When they arrived they demanded,

'Call Matiwane.' They did not say, 'Call the chief to us.'

So they called him and an induna pointed him out to them saying, 'This, my chiefs, is Matiwane.'

Then the English asked him, 'Have you not enough in the meat of cattle? Do you then also eat that of men?'

'How so, my chiefs?' he asked.

'We say so because people report that when they subject

themselves to you, you kill them. The Government has told us
to ask you what offence those people have committed.'

To this Matiwane replied, 'I kill them because when I ask
them for food they refuse to give it me, and so I simply take it
for myself by force.'

'To this action of yours the Government replies that you
must pay these people an indemnity of seven thousand head of
cattle, for it does not appear that they have committed any
crime.'

The induna brought this message to the chief, 'Chief, there is
bad news (lit. 'an army is at our back'). These folk demand that
seven thousand head of cattle be produced and paid to those
tribes as an indemnity.'

Matiwane then replied that he would give an answer next
day, and forthwith summoned together all the great ones of the
AmaNgwane and told them that he had been fined seven
thousand head by the commando.

'But,' said he, 'I myself think this is far too much. Why did
they, seeing they were powerless, refuse me food when I
demanded it?' And he added, 'As for me I don't see why I
should comply and furthermore I don't know what sort of arms
they have got.'

(Matiwane agrees to pay an indemnity.)

The AmaNgwane remonstrated with him, 'Do you see that
shiny weapon (field gun) standing there, of which you can't see
how they fight with it? Are you (merely) the equal in value of
an ox? (i.e. are you not much more valuable than cattle?) For
seeing that even Shaka did not get your cattle, as we refused to
hand them over, they are still there in full strength. And as to
those chiefs on whose account you are now troubled, you picked
from them only the fat cattle, and so there are many cattle-
kraals still quite full. No, give them what they ask for, sir.'

'Well, who is there that knows the country around Grahamstown? Call them all together and ask who they are.'

They told him, 'Sir, his name is Mlotsha of the AmaBhele.'

'Go and tell them that I agree and shall being the cattle.'

(Mlotsha's treachery.)

So they picked four men besides Mlotsha, 'You and you, go
with Mlotsha and drive these cattle, and do not disregard his

orders, for he is my deputy. Whoever shall disobey Mlotsha I shall kill.'

So they drove those seven thousand head of cattle, and slept once on the road, before arriving in the country of the Ama-Bhele, because, in fact, these people had been moved farther and farther off by Matiwane.

Then spoke Mlotsha, 'You see, maNgwane, this is how a village (i.e. great wealth) is acquired. Will you do as I tell you?'

To this the men replied, 'Of course, Mbhele, we would like to become rich but how can we do it? Seeing that we are simply marching along like this.'

He told them, 'Well, let us leave all these cattle with other people and return to the chief and say: Sir, we bring bad news; the order is that you must send another seven thousand head.'

They replied, 'Well, Mbhele, what can we say? Seeing that we were told that if we should ever dare to disobey you we would be slain, lest we disregard your orders. Be it done as you say, Mbhele.'

So he begged from the man who was in charge of his fellow-tribesmen there, that he, Mlotsha, might locate cattle amongst his people and when he had arranged the matter with him he promised him, 'I shall give you a share also if you will bear witness for me to those people to whom I am going to entrust cattle of mine', and so then he divided them.

Then they returned; when the people saw him they exclaimed,

'Hawu, is this Mlotsha back again? Is it possible, Mlotsha, that you have come right from Grahamstown?' and the order was given, 'Call him and those other men that went with him, so that Matiwane may hear the news soon.'

'Good day, Mlotsha.'

'Ndabezitha! I have been running and hastening all the way.'

'Do you now come right from there?'

'Yes, sir, just so.'

"Tell me, my child, what did they say?'

'Hawu, sir, I have bad news, for they say you must add another seven thousand head. We told them that the chief had not heard about fourteen thousand head, but they said that we had to go back to fetch them, for the chief had not understood properly.'

The councillors urged him, 'Yes, chief, let these be added to the others', but he refused saying, 'You maNgwane, did you not hear them when they demanded seven thousand from me?'

'Yes, sir, we heard it very well.'

'Well, how then am I to produce these? Let them come and take them for themselves.'

(Second commando against Matiwane.)

The white men waited and waited, but no cattle came. Then messengers were sent to summon Mlotsha and the men who had gone with him, but they found the dough already dry on the grinding stone and only flies (not cattle) lowed in the cattle-kraal of Mlotsha (i.e. the village was absolutely deserted), and so also in those of the men that had gone with him. The Government waited and waited but nothing happened.

The commando got impatient and said, 'But this chief Matiwane is slighting us.' Thus passed almost a year but the cattle did not appear.

'To arms!' and off the commando went. It arrived with the message, 'The Government ordered us to come to you, Matiwane, to ask why you have delayed so long in sending those seven thousand head of cattle that a year has almost passed? What really is your intention?'

'No, sirs, I have sent them already.'

The English replied, 'We have not seen them.'

So then messengers were sent to summon Mlotsha together with those men that he had taken with him, but their kraals were found to be empty and the runners returned to report the same thing as before, that they had found only dogs left behind. Now the commando went to Mlotsha's and when he and his people saw it they ran away and scattered.

(Matiwane refuses to pay.)

The men said to Matiwane, 'Chief, the cattle are there, they cover the whole plain, they are not worth yourself. You see now what has been done by those people of yours (viz. Mlotsha and his folk); and you see this commando which is threatening us now. What do you perceive things with? (i.e. have you no reason left), for behold your people (i.e. Mlotsha *cum suis*) have fled. Don't you realize that the cattle are with them? It seems to us that you are becoming foolish. We told you to leave alone

those tobacco-rolls of Mshweshwe and not to use the snuff, for
we always knew that he was an evildoer. And we told you to
distribute those jackal-karosses amongst the great ones, but not
to wear them yourself. But you disregarded us and wore them,
and you took the tobacco, and so now there is no manhood left
in you. Don't you see that the cattle (with which to pay the
fine) are there with your people? It were better for you to take
them and hand them over to the white men.'

But no, Matiwane flatly refused with the words, 'No,
maNgwane, this I cannot do again; I have already paid, and it
doesn't matter now what comes after.' So he refused and that
was the end of it.

'You have continually worried me, you white folk, now take
the cattle yourself, for I with my own hands shall never give
them to you,' he said to the white men.

Scarcely had he spoken this when the English said, 'He is
getting insolent and ignores us, maintaining obstinately that he
sent us the cattle, though he never did so.' So they told him,
'The Government thanks you for your reply; but the Government did not wish to destroy you.'

'To destroy whom?' Matiwane replied in anger. Then
suddenly there was a rustling as when locusts come (i.e. a
muttering of disapproval amongst the English), for they passed
the word to one another that he was not going to hand over the
cattle willingly.

However, the night passed, and next morning the commando
sent word, 'We are others, and not those that were sent first.
The Government told us to inquire from you whether this reply
actually came from yourself, that the Government must come
and take these cattle by force, and that you will never hand over
those cattle that the Government demands.'

To this Gungunyathi replied, 'You have continually been
nagging at me; I have no longer anything new to say, I have
spoken, I have done.' They said, 'Very well, we have heard and
we thank you.'

(Battle at Mbholompo[1])

Next morning early the white men were amongst the cattle
to drive them away and the armies began fighting and came to

---

[1] There is an account of the battle by a survivor recounted in Ellenberger's
History of the Basuto, 1912, pp. 187-8.

grips. They carried on this warfare until a year had passed, and the white men were much reduced in numbers, nor any longer so numerous as when the war started, for they had been thinned out by the spear, and so when they went into the forests to recuperate, they were surprised to see how few they had become, and realized acutely: 'the niggers are finishing us off.'

So they returned to the attack with a new stratagem, but they were not successful until two years had passed. Then in the third year the white men set fire to the bush. The forests burned, the country never having known fire before, the wood was dry and white. Then there were burnt even the very roots, and the army of the AmaNgwane now weakened and commenced to retreat; they remained in hiding in the forests, they who had been wont to issue forth continually.

(The AmaNgwane scatter.)

While all this was happening, Mphayise had broken off a large section of the tribe and led it elsewhere. Mphayise the son of Masumpa sought sanctuary with Faku, the chief of the AmaMpondo. Then also Nsimango, son of Masumpa, was no longer there, having gone to subject himself to the chief of the AmaXhosa. And Khondlo, son of Masumpa, was no longer there, for all those had broken off with sections of the Ama-Ngwane, and so he had also sought safety with Faku, the chief of the AmaMpondo. Thus while their kinsmen thought them dead because it seemed they had been destroyed by the fire, actually they had simply fled for safety with those princes who had been annoyed because Matiwane had opposed them when they told him, 'Those cattle belong to your own people,[1] we for our part are tired of fighting for nothing, so it were best for you to remain by yourself and fight your own battles.'

He himself also realized now that they had been beaten; however, if the AmaNgwane had sued for peace, they would have remained unharmed and would have settled down again, and nobody knows (what would have happened further); but as it was, they fled and became scattered.

[1] i.e. the subject tribes have enough cattle that we could take away and use to pay the indemnity.

5

Ngoma-lungundu

From *The Copper Miners of Musina and the Early History of the Zoutpansberg*. Edited (and supplemented by other material) by N. J. van Warmelo, Government Printer, Pretoria. Venda text by E. Mudau.

The Venda live in the northern Transvaal and southern part of Southern Rhodesia.

I

THE ancestors of the Vhavenḓa were very fond of songs and musical instruments of various sorts. Different instruments were played by men and women, and they were especially fond of collective music-making, when ecstatic scenes might be witnessed. Such occasions were for instance when the whole people foregathered to dance matangwa and tshikona, the young men danced and perspired, and the girls sat in the centre watching them, whilst relieving one another at the drums, the older females pranced about and trilled and the old men squatted around the beer pots and enjoyed themselves. These are things that every Venḓa child of today still knows from personal experience. In all the rites of initiation, such as Vhusha and Domba, the drums also played a most important part.

Amongst all their musical instruments, however, the greatest and that which was feared and revered most by all the people, was the instrument of the royal ancestor spirits, the Drum of Mwali, the ancestor God of the VhaSenzi and the Vhakalanga. This drum was called the Voice of the great God, Mambo wa Denga (King of Heaven), the Lord of all the ancestor spirits.

2

We have seen that the most important musical instruments were the drums, and amongst the drums again the greatest one of all was called Ngoma-lungundu or Thundundu. The people honoured it and feared it because it was believed to be the drum of the dead.

It was brought hither by the VhaSenzi, who are today

called VhaVenḓa. It is said that the drum belonged to their departed ancestors at the time when they were still living at Matongoni, yonder up North, in a country of great rivers and lakes, in a country of dense forests and jungles; a country overflowing with water and with many forests and fruit, of bananas growing in many groves and of tubers and peanuts in great variety. In that country lay the old dwelling sites of the Vha-Senzi and VhaLemba, who later came hither to Zoutpansberg to the country of the original VhaVenḓa who were called VhaNgoṋa. The chief of the latter was Tshivhula, whom the VhaSenzi, upon their arrival, accompanied by the VhaLemba, drove away; and he went westwards and settled in what is today Hananwa, around the Blauwberg.

The Chief kraal of the VhaNgoṋa was called Ha Raphulu. It was situated on the mountains of Vuvha near the small hill called Tshivheulwa. This place the VhaVenḓa fear even today; and on the ancient kraal sites of the VhaÑgoṋa they do not build, for that is tabu. This is because the VhaSenzi were the enemies of the VhaNgoṋa.

All the VhaNgoṋa are said to have come into this country in very ancient times. The people whom they already found in occupation were the VhaLembethu of Ha Mutele, those who exorcise the malombo spirits. Their chief was Mutele himself. Others of the same race were the people of Makuya and Thengwe.

All these tribes had different sorts of musical instruments. The VhaLemba had the *deze* (with metal tongues) and a kind of drum that was beaten for the rites of the circumcision lodge. The VhaNgoṋa had the xylophone. Matangwa is something new in this country, having first been taken up by Magoro's people.

Ngoma-lungundu was the sacred drum of the VhaSenzi, who had brought it with them from the north, from Matongoni or 'The Graves'.

Their king was greatly feared by all his people, for he could work miracles with this drum which they called the drum of the gods. His village was built on a mountain, and was of tremendous size. Its walls were built with huge stones; it was impregnable. The houses were built of shining slabs.

The drum itself was never seen by anybody except the high priest and the king. A special house had been built for it of beautiful slabs. This building was huge, so big that many thousands of people could not fill it. The roof was constructed of huge logs cut in the forests. In one chamber was placed the sacred thing itself, namely Ngoma-lungundu, the drum of Mwali.

3

The king was called by the name Mwali, and the high priest was known as Dzomo-la-Dzimu, the mouthpiece of God. To him the king gave directions to transmit to the people. He it was who could be seen, for Mwali himself was tabu to look upon. The drum Ngoma-lungundu also was beaten only by him and by the king.

Whenever the councillors heard a trumpet sound, they assembled in the courtyard and awaited what announcement was going to be made by the king through the mouth of the high priest. When they were all assembled there, the drum would be heard once. All the people would fall on their faces and make humble obeisance saying, 'Great king, male elephant, light of the country, great ancestor spirit, ruler of heaven.'

No man was permitted to see the king, they merely heard what he spoke to the high priest in a tremendous voice that reverberated in a terrifying manner.

The king usually spoke from his private hut which might not be visited by anyone. The place was guarded by his lions. Snakes with a head at either end kept all the fences to the sacred place closed. The lions were called the dogs of the king; whenever they heard the sacred drum, they began roaring in a terrifying way, praising their master.

Indeed, this king was indeed very sacred, so that they treated him as a god or an ancestor spirit. If the rain did not come the councillors came to the high priest and begged for it. He would then hear their prayers and transmit them to the king. Then there would be heard the drumming of Ngoma-lungundu, the lions would respond with their roaring, and this would show that their words had reached the king and had been well received. Then the trilling of the women would respond to the roaring of the lions and all the people would assemble. A great din would commence.

Then when the drum sounded again, a dead silence fell.

Mwali began to speak in a tremendous voice that was heard through the city of Matongoni. Every person would be seated with his eyes on the ground, covering up his face, because of the tabu that forbade people to gaze on his countenance. All the people, womenfolk included, were under a strict tabu not to look at him. Whosoever should gaze at him was immediately slain. The high priest also was not looked in the face, but with him the fear was not so great as with the king.

Ngoma-lungundu also was tabu to people, it might not be looked at, and the drum-stick with which it was beaten was equally tabu. He who beat the drum was the high priest himself, a man from the blood of the VhaSenzi. Before beating the drum, he would kneel at the door and salute the great drum. Then he would enter but remain on his knees and make obeisance and say, 'Great spirit, my master and of people and of animals and everything! You, omen of clouds, drum of the spirits, god of the heavens!' Then only would he take the drum-stick and beat softly, so that people who were far away could not hear it.

Those who heard it would be the princes within the royal precincts near to the house of the drum. They would immediately raise shouts of rejoicing that the people of the city must prepare themselves and rejoice before the drum. Then all at once the ululations of all the royal city would be heard around. Upon hearing this shouting of the princes throughout the town, all the people would remain quiet to hear the noise of Ngoma-lungundu. This was their way of honouring the drum of the gods. For the drum also the people regarded as a mudzimu, even as they feared Mwali himself as if he were an ancestor spirit.

Then the royal precincts would again echo to the blowing of sable horns. Suddenly the noise of the ancestor drum would be heard, making the whole hill resound, the hill of the ancestor spirits that was tabu to all men excepting the high priest and Mwali himself. Thereupon all the people would ululate, the men and youths using all the instruments they had, sable trumpets, impala horns, bugles, flutes, whistles and so forth and making a tremendous din all over the hill.

4

All this would take a long time, until at last silence would supervene when the trumpet sounding from the sacred place

was heard. This was a signal to the people to be silent, that
Mwali might speak and lay his laws and injunctions upon his
people, thundering the while with the noise of many waters
rushing over a cataract. His interpreter was the high priest himself. When all the people were silent, the drum would again be
heard, the people would fall on their knees and salute the king.
Then in complete silence of man and beast, the king spoke from
his sanctum near the hill. What he said was not understood, for
it was more like the great roaring of a heavy rain. Clouds were
seen hovering over the mountain, blackening in a fearsome manner. Above this black cloud, a fire could be seen leaping and blaz-
ing. Lightning played and flashed. Then the voice said, 'Hear
me, my children, I speak of great things, especially to you the
councillors and great ones all! Abandon all your differences
and quarrels, above all you, my children, born of my wives. You
are the ones that set the people against one another, because you
leave not your bickerings. The thieving amongst you exceeds all
measure. The people groan under the burden of your government.

'And you also, councillors and great ones of the tribe, listen
well. You also are bringing to ruin all the country by raising up
factions amongst my people. You have made laws which I,
your ancestor, did not give you. Listen you, grandchildren and
great-grandchildren, both male and female, and you all my
daughters' children. To all of you I say, leave off from bickering
and quarrelling, and from all evil.

'If you do not, I shall afflict you. If you hear not what I say,
I shall go forth from your midst. I shall vanish and go to live
beneath the earth. From thence I shall slay you all with an
earthquake. I shall cause you to sink away with all your cattle.
Listen carefully, all of you! Give ear to me, your ancestor; do as
your great-grandfathers did before you, whom I governed in
peace. They always hearkened to me with care, but now you live
in factions and in quarrelsomeness.'

The voice of the great-grandfather was not easily understood,
for he was a very aged man. He was indeed greatly aged, for all
the old men of the country were his grandchildren. Yet though
he was thus aged, his voice was very loud.

The pronouncement of the king having ended and having
been translated through the mouth of the high priest, the

sacred drum was beaten loudly, all the people trembled and fell to the ground in their terror, many of them fainted with fear and fell to the ground unconscious and never awoke again.

Those that remained were weak with terror of that which Mwali had spoken in his anger. Their fear was increased by a shaking of the earth, lightning and thunder in the cloud that covered the mountain and a great fire that blazed and shone over them.

The sharp voice of the high priest was heard above it all. Many of those who had died were old men and women of the VhaSenzi. Of the VhaLemba, however, not one had died, for they had been observant of the law.

What struck terror into people was that especially the sons of princes had been slain. Those who survived were very few.

Next morning at sunrise it was seen how many were the deaths. There was a calling to one another to come and look; in every household there was a weeping, for Mwali had slain people with the noise of Ngoma-lungundu, the drum of magic and of slaughter.

This was the rod with which the old man punished his people. The noise of this drum worked miracles.

6

The Traditional History of the Budya

Translated from the Shona by Professor G. Fortune from a
text originally published in *Citanhatu*, Chishawasha Press,
Salisbury, Southern Rhodesia.

The Budya are a Shona-speaking people now living in the Mtoko
District of Southern Rhodesia which is in the north-east corner of
this country. To the east of them are found the Sena-speaking
Barwe-Tonga, to the north and west the Tavara and Korekore.
Their language and culture has been described to some extent in the
following articles and books:

Doke, Clement M. *A Comparative Study in Shona Phonetics*, The
  University of the Witwatersrand Press, Johannesburg, 1931.
Morkel, E. R. 'The mondoro or ancestral spirit of the Wabuja,
  Mtoko', *NADA*, viii (1930), 11–14.
—— 'Spiritualism among the Wabudya', *NADA*, xi (1933), 106–16.
Wieschhoff, H. A. 'Marriage among the Babudja in Southern
  Rhodesia', *Twenty-fifth Anniversary Studies*, ed. D. S. Davidson,
  Philadelphia Anthropological Society, 1937, pp. 221–35.
—— 'Names and naming customs among the Mashona in Southern
  Rhodesia', *AA*, xxxix (1937).
—— 'Consecration of the grain among the Barwe of Moçambique',
  Ethnos (1938), 81–83.
—— 'The Zimbabwe-Monomotapa culture in South-east Africa',
  GSA, viii (1941), 1–120.

ALL the Budya people are of the *Shumba* or *Haro* totem. Their
praise names are *Nyamuziwa*, *Bondai*. When praising their
ancestors they say, *Bonga, Varimatswavo*. For an oath they say,
Njapayu. If you hear a person taking an oath in this way, you
will know that he is a Shumba of Mutoko's country, and further
that he is a real Budya; for there are many people living in
Mutoko's country who have different totems and praise-names.
They are not Budya.

The Budya came from Mingare. This country is far beyond
the part called Tete. From Tete, on your way there, you travel
through very many districts indeed. That land is to the north
and a little to the east of Mutoko's country where the Budya
people live now. And according to current opinion, no one
knows very much about where they lived before they came to
that country called Mingare.

At that time the father of the Budya, their leader and judge,
a man whose renown was well known by many of the black
people, was called Nehoreka. Nehoreka signifies *hooking* or
linking like a fish-hook which hardly ever lets go what it has
caught. The reference is to the fact that he would never allow
to be taken away from him a country or goods which had fallen
into his hands. He would choose to die rather than to let what
was his be taken by other tribes. Furthermore he used to insist
on what he had said being done straight away. If it was not
done, there was no good in store for those who had neglected to
do it. They were harried in a pitiful way, enough to dry the
saliva in your mouth. Sometimes they would be killed on the
spot.

Nehoreka lived for a long time in his country, Mingare, but
after that he realized that his country no longer pleased him.
One day Nehoreka thought of migrating, leaving his country
and going to another land, on account of the fact that, in the
district where he was, there was no longer any water. The
livestock was perishing of thirst. The people too had begun to
be short of water, both for drinking and washing. They had a
very hard time of it when the spring came round, when all the
rivers and wells were dry. They were unable to make any of
their rice or vegetable gardens in the spring season. And the
food supply, both for men and beasts, was short. Hence
Nehoreka gathered all his people one day and said to them:
'Look, my children, I, your father, am no longer content to live
in this waterless country. I am no longer prepared to live as a
messenger, a servant, an outsider. I want to seek another country
where I shall live without troubles, relaxed and at peace with
my family, without annoyance or hindrance or anything to
trouble me. And you, my children, would it not please you too
to find a land like that?' His whole family cried saying, 'Hee
father! If we were just to see a country like that we would be

very happy. We would say that we were indeed blessed. No one can want to live in this country, desert and treeless as it is.'

Then Nehoreka said, 'My children, my princes, your answer has pleased me much. But before migrating as a tribe, we, some few cautious and fearless men and myself, want first to go and seek that place so that, having found it, we may return and go there all together, straight to the land we desire.

'But remember my sons, that we have now conceived for ourselves, have now undertaken for ourselves, a truly hard task. Keep this in mind that we shall have to make war on those people who have the coveted land. Now in that war we shall lose very many of our kinsmen.' His children replied, 'Father, choose quickly some cautious and brave men and go on your search for a beautiful land. That is what we want; but the war you are speaking of to us, we say it is our porridge, we do not fear to die.'

Spying out the Land

And now Nehoreka and some few cautious men prepared for their journey from Mingare, to go and seek a good land. But before starting, they began to ask one another in what direction they should go. Many of them said, 'Let us go with our faces to the north.' But Nehoreka and a few others said, 'Let us make straight for the south.' And everyone chose to go in the direction chosen by their chief.

During his journey, Nehoreka passed through many countries. He first arrived in the country called Nyamanzawa, and he spent a few days exploring all over. But that country did not please him. So he left it and went to Marembe's land. He did not stay in there, he merely passed through it. After leaving Marembe, he passed through these countries: Mukachameno, Mbeza, Nyangowe, Michima, and Ngahwe. He did not stop many days in those countries. What he merely used to do was, in any country which he happened to reach, to spend one or two days looking carefully everywhere to see if that country was a pleasant one. Now in all the lands through which he passed, he did not see one that satisfied his eyes. But then he reached a certain country which was the domain of a chief called Makate, owner of many cattle and goats. He had built his towns on the hills, whole collections of homesteads, houses standing out like rocks on the hill-tops. His village was built on some small hills near the large mountain called Mutemwa which is near the hospital where lepers are treated.

Nehoreka walked all over, exploring and examining every place in that country. He saw fine arable land for fields and rice gardens. He also saw extensive marches with green reeds and fine grass for livestock. And that land had rivers full of water. Then he looked all round and saw hills, he climbed the hills and found they had honey in them among the rocks, and bees and halictus insects of various kinds. He stopped and uncovered a rock and there was honey clear to see and plentiful. He had just to eat it. After this he said to the men who were with him, 'Look my boys, this is the country I have been seeking; look, in this land, there is everything I want. This land is full of honey and milk, rice and sweet-reed, millet and fruit, water and grass and land. Also there are shafts, caverns and big caves into which we can run and hide, when fleeing from war. Another thing that has pleased me very much on account of these mountains is this, that I shall be able to build my town high up as Makate here has done so that on the arrival of an armed band, I may be able to see it far away. Then also the honey in these parts is not hard to extract. All you have to do is to overturn a rock. You have not to look for an axe to cut it at all. Let us now return to our country, go and fetch our companions, and come out for I have found the land I longed to see, a land which I love, beautiful to look at, which pleased me and fulfils all my longing.'

Then Nehoreka went back to his own country with the desire for that new land piercing him, distracting him, giving him no sleep. He travelled night and day without resting; he used only to rest while eating. And so he reached his country quite lean and drawn, with sunken eyes: his whole body had become wasted and emaciated, leaving only his head.

As soon as ever Nehoreka arrived in his country, before he had drawn breath or set down the burden from his shoulders, before he had entered his house or been greeted by his people, he gathered his tribe together and said to them, 'My children, I have found the land which I have sought for so long. I have seen the land which is the end of all searching, the land which at once gives my eyes their satisfaction. I cannot relate to you, cannot speak to you with words alone about the beauty of that land so that you may properly appreciate it because you have not yet seen so beautiful a country since you were born. Even those who came with me, on seeing it, stared and stared with open mouths looking out and contemplating its beauty. But now, my children, I am telling you that the affair is a heavy one indeed; and dry as a husk to take that country and make it ours, for its master has people who outnumber us as do the ants. In my view, if we try to fight him, few as we are, we would completely perish, being killed in the battle. We would all die, being killed like flies. So I think a good thing would be this, for me first to go to Choma, where I gave the brideprice for my wife, and ask my father-in-law kindly to give me some soldiers to help us fight Makate.'

Choma is a country near Mingare, that is where Nehoreka had married. He had married a daughter of Dzivaguru, the chief of Choma, who was feared by many people for they believed he had the power to cause rain to fall or to withhold it. Before resting, Nehoreka passed on to Choma and went to his father-in-law and said, 'Father, I have come as your child to tell you that my country is very difficult to live in; there is no longer sufficient water, and your grand-children are dying of thirst. There are no pastures for the animals, or plots for cultivating, any more. My family and my stock are dying off wholesale through hunger and thirst. I tried to find a suitable country to which to migrate with my family and I have found one. That land belongs to a certain chief called Makate. It has agricultural land, pastures, water, hills on which to build our houses, and caves in which to hide from raiders. There are many wonderful things there, all of which I cannot tell you now. So my idea, father, is to attack Makate, and drive him from his country so that it may become mine. Can you please give me some men to help me fight him? For if I attack him with my band alone I would not be able to overcome him at all because he has a great number of people, many more than mine.'

Dzivaguru listened to all this and said, 'My son, you should not worry yourself like this. I, your father, am still wide awake, still have my senses; I haven't yet given up eating beans, not yet dead, still alive. This news you have brought—I like it, it attracts me a lot. I, too, your father, have no longer any sense of

ease in my country here for people have increased a great deal.
So it is difficult to find where to cultivate and where to pasture
the cattle. I am also having to look for a piece of territory to
relieve the pressure on my family. I'll give you these soldiers to
help you attack Makate but, when you have overcome him, you
must slice off a small place for me where my family may over-
flow.'

Nehoreka accepted the soldiers, paid his thanks, and went
back happily to his own country. When he reached his country
he straightaway gathered his people together the same day and
said to them, 'See, my sons, I have brought these others to help
us fight Makate. Now you too get all your things ready; the day
after tomorrow we are off to attack that man.' So all Nehoreka's
people set to busily, getting their equipment in order. That day
there was no more calling anyone who could be expected to hear
such was the hubbub in all the houses.

Nehoreka's Journey

When the Budya left their country they did not all come out,
all at once, on the same day. The old people and the sick were
told, 'Stay meanwhile; we shall come and fetch you when we
have won.' Sufficient food was left for them and a few people to
look after them. The journey of Nehoreka and his tribe was a
pleasure to anyone who saw them on their migration. As they
went they sang the *tsotsa* and the *maguu*, these are songs of long
ago. In these the women sing the leading parts, the men the
accompanying refrain, both joining in complementary verse
and chorus, with shrill cries of applause going up from the
women, drums beating, children chattering, cattle lowing,
goats bleating, there was an uproar for you. Then, too, there
would be those who pranced in the air, those who danced and
still others who leaped over the bushes. Some big fellows ran
ahead and threw themselves down on the ground, getting up
and shaking themselves in a way which made everyone marvel,
mouth dry of saliva, while some of the women would cavort
around with axes and choppers in their hands. Up the dust
would fly, there would be a dark mist — it would get quite dark.

Nehoreka and his followers did not destroy or attack the
people whose countries they traversed while on their way. He
didn't even speak with the people of those countries. The

Budya never used to want to speak to other tribes because they used to say 'we cannot speak with servants or minions'. They were people with a great sense of their own importance, they thought a lot of themselves and praised themselves. They never considered a person or even a chief of another country; they thought they were the lords of the whole world.

Fighting Makate

Nehoreka and his people spent very many days while on their way to Makate's country. Eventually they reached it and then Nehoreka said to his followers, 'Now you have seen the land I spoke of. Look ahead, and behind, and on both sides, and contemplate the full beauty of it.' His children looked all over and saw to their wonder the rivers overflowing, full to the brim with the water which had troubled them so much. Abundant grass and land and many other things sated their hungry eyes and they said to their father, 'Truly this is the country which needs us to live in it.'

Then Nehoreka said, 'Look, my children, since you are pleased with this country we are going to make some trouble in these days. The day after tomorrow my plan is to attack that man, chase him out and take this country so that it becomes ours. Look, my chiefs, these are days of danger and distress. We shall not eat food which drops easily into our stomachs. We shall not eat and drink water, we shall not eat cooked food, we shall not sleep and take full rest until we have overcome that man. So get your bows ready, with arrows and spears and battleaxes, because the time is near when we must fight like the lion which is our totem.'

On the following day Nehoreka drew up his force to attack Makate. Then they got up very early in the morning and climbed on to the mountain where Makate and his people dwelt. Makate's people were asleep, unaware that their enemies were ready to kill them. However, although Makate and his people were taken unawares, they were not overcome, not at all. Makate was no fool or simpleton, but a clever man. He knew that, although the times were peaceful, a band of his enemies would one day come. For in those days, so long ago, the land was ruled by the spear.

So Makate told his people before the event, saying 'Beware

my children, there is much suffering on its way to this country. Keep your weapons ready, do not live or sleep like stupid men. Keep alert, awake, on your guard, expecting and waiting for the day or danger which is coming. I, your father, do not know at all the hour or the day when that trial will come, but I know for sure that a great calamity is drawing near. So, from this day forward be watchful and beware until the day arrives. So my last words are these. Let every man keep a drum or something he can sound in his house so that whoever hears or sees this danger coming may immediately give whatever alarm he can to alert the others. So from today on there must be no one found beating or sounding anything unless he has seen something that gives alarm.'

From that day Makate's people kept ears pricked up and eyes open, watching with close attention for what was coming. They no longer ate anything tasty, they were living in a state of extreme alert. As for sleeping, they were now keeping watch, both man and wife in the house; first the wife would sleep, with the husband keeping a watch lest anything approach outside and then, when he was tired, he would waken his wife so that she should listen for anything coming in the night while he was asleep. They continued like this until it was dawn outside. These people suffered in a way which called out for all to see, their eyes as a result bloodshot with lack of sleep, like people suffering with a sickness of the eyes.

So when Nehoreka's people entered Makate's village they were heard at once by some of Makate's people, who were listening lest something should come outside. On hearing something creeping outside, they looked out through the holes in their huts and saw, to their dismay, that things had taken a fearful turn, the whole village was surrounded by their enemies. Immediately they beat their drums and immediately Makate's people leapt up, snatched up their weapons and poured outside. Listen and hear the turmoil made by axes and choppers, look and see the confusion made by spears and arrows. War had broken out and the fighting lasted a long time as they pierced and cut one another with arrows, spears, knives, and battle-axes, some rolling others to the precipices, some burning others with fire, some striking others with stones in the hand. After a while Nehoreka's men realized that their kinsmen had suffered many losses and so they fled, running down the mountain. But when they were at the bottom Nehoreka said to them: 'Stop fleeing, climb up the hills and try to kill that man and his people because, unless you kill or conquer him, we cannot take his country.'

So then the Budya went up the mountain again, anxious to try and attack again. Then Makate's people rolled rocks down on them and crushed them. Some of them died on the spot, others lost a foot, and others were chafed by the rocks. Nehoreka's men realized now that they would not be able to climb up the mountain again, with their kinsmen being slaughtered to right and left, and so they began to flee. And then Makate's force pushed them, following after and shooting them with arrows and crushing them with stones. When Nehoreka's party had been driven far off, Makate's followers returned home, exultant that they had overcome their enemies. Their chief was very happy at this victory and said to them, 'You have seen now the threat about which I warned you in time. Now settle down and relax as there is no one to spy on you or trouble you, for you have overcome my enemies and yours.'

But some of them began to weep and moan because their kinsmen had been killed in the battle. So Makate said to them, 'Do not weep or be troubled in your hearts because the death of your kinsmen has saved the country; therefore I say to you, help one another to build the houses; whoever has a house which was burnt in the battle, must be helped to rebuild it.'

When Nehoreka realized clearly what the flight of the Budya meant, after they had failed to overpower Makate's force, he was overcome with disappointment. He gathered his following together and said to them, 'Look, my children, today is the most disappointing day I have ever spent since ever I was born, because it has never yet been heard of, nor yet happened, that the Budya were overcome in battle. But what has happened today has made me suffer, has made my body strengthless, has appalled me and left me without a plan. I no longer know what course to adopt. And see here further, the worst thing is this that we shall not now be able to take that man's country because he has overcome us.'

Many of Nehoreka's people thought of returning to their own country, Mingare. Many of them said, 'Since we have failed to conquer this man, it is better for us to return whence we came; for if we stay in this country, there will be no good result. Makate will pursue us with his army and kill us in the end. Let us go quickly before he has the idea of following us.'

Nehoreka was not willing to return to his country and he said to his people, 'My children, I, your father, want nothing of this turning our face again towards the land of tribulation; and I am not willing to allow anyone to return thither. This is what I am thinking, let us seek for a plan with which to overcome Makate and simply drive him from his country. I choose rather that we should all die in battle than that we should return again to the land of our suffering.'

Nehoreka's people began to murmur and to grumble, to frown and to sulk; and they said, 'What use is it to try and fight again with men who have overcome us? Since we failed to conquer them when we were many, how can we conquer them now, few as we are?'

So then Nehoreka said to them, 'Look here and see! The thing that surprised and astounded me is this. When we fought with Makate we were much more numerous than his people! How did it happen then that he beat us? Surely he did not beat us on the score of strength—but what he had I know not. And now, before fighting him for the second time I want to know his strategy first of all, all he had which caused him to overcome us. I think that if we gave him a handsome present to please him, he would easily reveal to us his charms.'

The people of old, though they had their wisdom, had many false beliefs. Of course there are many things in this world which have unsuspected powers, greater than our human powers, lightning, wind, water and many other things. But then people believed that they could make use of certain powers, they knew not what, and increase their own strength by using horns of various kinds and magical tricks, and that they could thus overcome their enemies. And if they lost these things or had them taken away from them, they would lose courage and say, 'Ah, there is no hope for me.' And they would think only of flight. Nehoreka and Makate were like that.

Nehoreka spoke again. 'A fine present would be to give him a wife to marry so that we could say to him, "Now you are our son-in-law, we no longer want to fight any more." Nehoreka thought that if he were to give Makate a wife, he would be very happy. Furthermore, he thought that a wife is something that is loved more than anything else; she might be told all the small secret things lying under his heart, all the hidden things. She might be told all about the magical charms and medicine horns. 'And when she had seen them she would then come and tell me; and when she had taken them, she would give them to me. And I would then use them until I had overcome that man.'

One day Nehoreka took his sister who was so beautiful that all should come and see her. He took her to Makate and said to him there, 'My friend, take this woman and marry her. We did very wrong in attacking you. Now I am giving you this wife to be a sign that you and I are become one in sympathy, with no anger, spite or jealousy for one another. And further I ask you please to grant me a little place to live in with my family.'

Makate accepted that wife gladly not knowing that 'there was relish under the porridge', unaware that all the time a trap was being set for him to catch him. Further he gave Nehoreka a place to live in with his family.

Makate lived with that wife for a very long time and saw that her ways were pleasing. So to show her that he loved her much, he began to let her keep things that were very dear to him. He showed her many other things which he believed enabled him to defeat those who attacked him, and he taught her also their use.

Makate's Flight

When that wife realized that she had seen all the things which Makate used, one day, seeing that Makate was not at home, but gone to look up his kinsmen, gathered them all up and took them to her brother.

Nehoreka gathered all his tribe together and said to them, 'Now be glad because everything, the kingdom and the riches and the land that is Makate's, is in your hands. Everything is ours. See all these things. Therein lies Makate's whole strength. Now rejoice because we are able to overcome him and drive him from his country and make it ours. There is nothing that he has to conquer us with because we have all his power in our hands.' Then Nehoreka said to his men, 'Form a file and let us go to destroy Makate's kingdom.' So they went quietly without a word. Makate saw them while they were still far off and said to his children who were near him, 'Look at those people, they astonish me. Why are they coming here unannounced and silently like those who come from the graves, to bury a dead man?'

The sight surprised and troubled him in his heart and he spoke again. 'Truly I know not what evil thing they are coming to do. If they were on business of a good nature, they would be talking as they came. But the way in which they are acting, their way of approaching like robbers and thieves, the throne is slipping from my grasp, the kingship is now without taste or relish, and now all my plans fail me. I remember, indeed, that the day on which they came to give me a wife, they talked as they came. They didn't come like baboons intent on entering a field. But if they are coming to attack me, I must now go and make ready my medicine horns. Today they want to know by experience that I am a real man, strong enough and not to be played with. So I mean to finish them all off and kill them.'

Then he went into the house where his horns were kept. He opened the door but found none of his instruments in there any more. All he could do was to stare. To his horror he saw that the place of his weapons was taken by a swarm of cockroaches and flies which had made their way in. He looked this way and that and cried, 'What has happened? Am I mad or am I dreaming?' Then he called the wife whom Nehoreka had given him. But there was no reply. So then he knew that she had fled with his property. He sat down and cried out aloud, 'Alas, my father, today indeed my fate is sealed. Today I am cast out to the winds, into the cold without a fire, without a blanket to cover me. What made me take such a monstrous woman? See the black treachery which has blotted me out, destroyed me today.'

So he came out of his house to find, alas, that things could not be worse, Nehoreka's band was already at the foot of the mountain. Makate then told his family, 'Put all your things together; let us quit this country, for we are no longer able to defeat the Budya, who have taken from me my magic calabashes and all my horns.' So then Makate's family gathered up their things and left at once in flight, unseen by the Budya. While Makate's people were gathering together their belongings, Nehoreka was trying to use Makate's magic tools so that they might help him.

However, they were of no use to him so he burnt them in the hearth and then the Budya climbed into the hills where Makate's village had been. They found the houses deserted. All they found were flies buzzing everywhere, but the people and stock had long since gone. Then they looked down to the bottom of the mountain, on the red plain, and saw Makate and his family already very far away. Quickly they descended the mountain and ran hard to catch Makate's family but they failed as they were already a great distance away. On their flight Makate and his family went straight to the east but no man saw where they went to. So the Budya said they went into a great outcrop of rock.

Makate's Rock

On his flight Makate came to a great rock floor. He took his tail-switch and struck it on the ground. The rock floor opened straight away and all his following entered in as a throng and disappeared into the earth. Makate remained outside waiting for the arrival of the Budya, who were still, all the while, tracking them down. When Makate saw that the Budya were near he called out with a loud voice and said, 'Remain and enjoy my land, you traitors. Though you may think that this land in which you now are in is a beautiful one, nevertheless it is surpassed by this new one here which I have entered with my family. But what I am telling you is this. Here at the place where I have gone in I am leaving a hoe without a handle, beaten into the rock, so that whoever comes by this way may see that this is where I have entered. But, be very careful lest any of you show this place to anyone. Whoever shows this place to anyone at all will be turned by me into something he doesn't yet know. I want whoever finds this place to find it on his own, without another to show him. If you keep these words of mine, you will be happy and prosperous in my country for a long time.'

Then Makate took off the hoe and beat it into the rock. Then he went down into the rock, which there and then closed up. The Budya came up to the rock floor there and sought for the place into which Makate and his family had gone, but they did not find it. Eventually they found the hoe beaten into the rock. They tried to pull it out and remove it, but they failed, so they returned to their home.

When they had got home, Nehoreka gathered everyone to-gether and said to them, 'You heard for yourselves and with your own ears what this man said. You heard him say that no one is to show that place where he went in to anyone else. If there is any one of you who has a loose tongue so as to chatter like a little bird in the forest, if he should want to tell another what he has seen or what he has heard, I know not what is in store for him. For my part, I am going to be as silent as the grave.'

There really is a rock floor into which Makate went. No Budya would show you the place, though you might give him a wife, or beer, or cattle, or meat, or money, because they are still afraid of Makate's last words. But many hunters of our own time have seen the place, only they are not willing to talk to anyone about it. It is said that the hoe which Makate left is still there today. If you try to pull it out you will find that it comes easily enough until it is almost free. Only then will it come no further, no matter how many people there are trying to remove it. Also the footprints of Makate's family and those of his stock are still on the rock. Even the marks of the baskets, put down on the rock when they were going in, are still visible.

What is amazing is how this man made the rock so soft, so that all this could be seen. Anyone who wants to see the place where Makate went in must go to Mtoko's country, reach All Souls' Mission, then travel to the east. He must go about ten miles towards Chimoyo's country, and then search for himself and on his own for the place where Makate went in. The sign which will tell him he has found the place will be the hoe on the rock-face. No Budya whatever may show that place to another. If a father knows it he never shows his son, nor a husband his wife, for they still remember Makate's words with fear.

The Four Uouas

From *The Folk Tales of Angola*, collected and edited by H.
Chatelain, American Folk-lore Society, 1894. Recorded from
Jelemfa dia Sabatelu. With notes on the text.

The Mbundu of Angola, from whom this story was collected, are the
most important of the Bantu-speaking peoples of that country,
numbering well over a million.

The Mbundu appear to divide their prose into five main categories:
the fictitious story, *musoso*, which seeks to entertain rather than
instruct; true stories, *maka*, which are instructive rather than otherwise; historical narratives, *malunda*; proverbs; and riddles.

This story, Chatelain comments, though not personifying an
animal nor relating any supernatural occurrence, is accounted a
musoso, because the case of four sisters taking the same name and
wanting a common husband appears at once to people to be an
invention. According to custom, Kimanaueze is the father of such
fictitious heroines, and as the tale accounts for the origin of the
custom that a man shall not marry his wife's sister, even after the
wife's death, it belongs to the class of aetiologic tales.

W E will tell of the four Uouas, of the elder two, and the younger
two. Na Kimanaueze kia Tumb'a Ndala, favourite of friends,
built, lived. He begat his four children; all females. There came
no male child. They all (had) one mother.

The eldest, when she came to name herself, said: 'I (am)
Uoua.'[1] Her younger who followed behind her, also said, 'I (am)
Uoua.' Their sister, the third, says, 'I (am) Uoua.' The youngest
the fourth, says, 'I (am) Uoua.' The other people say, 'The
name is one, that you called yourselves, in your sistership of
four. How shall they call you?'

They grew up; have come to the age of marrying.

There came a man to woo, to Uoua the eldest. They (were in)
one house, of virginity. They placed him in the guest house. The
sun died. They cooked food for him; he ate. The night came;
the man went out; he went to the house of the girls.

He says, 'Evening, you, ladies.' The girls accept it, saying,
'This is evening.' They spread for him a mat on the ground; he

---

[1] 'Uoua' signifies 'silliness, stupidity'.

sits down. The girls entertain him; saying, 'Thou spentest (the day) how, young man?' He says:[1]

> 'I spent the day as an elephant spends it.
> I played, as a player of backgammon.
> The elephant is lame, (because) they shot him.
> The path is worn down, (because) they walked it.
> A nice bottle of bird-seed, (is) food of birds.
> The wild fig-tree and the Mubangu tree (are)
>   ornaments of a home.
> In the East, we are children of the hippo;
> In the West, we are children of the Governor.
> The young man, when he covers himself,
> (Casts) the mantle over the left (shoulder).
> Staff, staff; sword, sword:
> Staff, we took it for ornament;
> The sword, we took it for sergeantship.
> The tobacco slept at head of bed;
> The palm-wine slept in the glass;
> Tobacco, (is) the cause of spitting;
> Palm-wine, (is) the cause of talking.
> There is where his heart went. This is the end, ladies.'

They say, 'We accept.' They say, 'Let us pass time. The sun is down, the evening dark. That thou thoughtest, saying, "I will go to give them (good) evening," we praise it, that thou didst so. The end.' He answered, saying, '(Is) of God.' They continue their conversation. He says, 'I came (because of) thee, thou, na Uoua the eldest.'

Na Uoua says, 'Very well. Thou shalt marry me, (if) thou marriest us all, the four of us. If thou thinkest, that (thou wilt have) me alone, the eldest, thou canst not marry me. It must be that we marry our one man, the four of us in the fourhood (of) one mother.' The man assents, saying, 'I can marry you.' He gives them tobacco; he goes to his guest house; sleeps.

At daybreak, he goes to na Kimanaueze, saying, 'I have come to have a talk; I want to marry with thy daughters.' Na Kimanaueze says, 'Very well. If thou canst afford the four of them, bring me the price.' The man agrees to, saying, 'I can. All right.'

---

[1] The following sentences are proverbs, puns, and figurative sayings, especially used by young folks in courting.

He returns to his home. He finds his father; says, 'Where I went, they accepted me. They asked me for the wooing-presents of four girls.' His father took up four mothers of cows; he gave them to him, saying, 'Go and woo.' He slept.

In the morning, he starts. He arrives at his parents-in-law's, he hands the cows. They accept. The bridegroom says, 'I give you four days. The fifth day I shall come to fetch the brides.' They cook him a mother of goat. He slept.

Morning comes; he returns to his home. He slept four days. The fifth day having come, the man took the companions. They go to fetch the brides; they arrive. They spent the day. They cooked them a goat and mush. The evening came; they gave them the brides.

They come with them. They introduce them into their houses. The eldest has her house; the younger has her house; the third has her house; the youngest has her house. They kill them a goat. They eat in the houses of brideship. The two days are over. The band of the companions scatters.

The man will not come into the houses of the brides. All days he is sleeping in the house of bachelorship. One day his father scolded him, saying, 'Thou, na Nzuá, the girls strangers, since thou hast brought them home, in their houses thou refusest to enter, why?' He replied to his father, saying, 'Father, shame has held me, because since I brought them home, they not yet ate nice food. Tomorrow I will go to the bush to hunt; perhaps I may there kill a deer for them to eat.' He slept.

When shone the morning, he took up his gun, and his knife, and his dog, and his boy. He says, 'Let us go to hunt.' They start; they arrive in bush. They build a hut; they get in. They sleep.

Morning shines. Na Nzuá goes to set traps for rats. He comes away; comes to his hut. He slept. They went to look at the traps. They loosened the rats; forty rats. They return to the grass-hut.

Na Nzuá tells his boy, saying, 'Cut green leaves.' The boy cuts leaves. He says, 'Bind four bundles of the rats.' He says, 'Boy, I will send thee directly home. Thou shalt arrive at night; do not arrive by day. These four bundles, carry them to my wives.'

The boy went. He begins with Uoua the eldest. He enters into the house, says, 'This bundle (is) that which the master sends thee, saying, "the bundle, which the wise bound, let a fool untie it. I remain here, I cannot yet go". He, the master, told me, saying, "this bundle, go, give it na Uoua the eldest; do not mention it to her sisters".' The boy went out.

He went again to Uoua the second; she opened to him. The boy said, 'The bundle here, master says, "the bundle which the wise bound let a fool untie it. Thou alone, I sent thee the bundle; thy sisters, do not mention it to them. I still remain".' The boy went out.

He went again to Uoua the third; she opened to him. He entered; 'Master says, "the bundle that the wise bound let a fool untie it. Thou only, I send thee this bundle; thy sisters, do not mention it to them".' The boy went out.

He went further to Uoua the youngest; she opened to him. The boy said, 'Master says, "this bundle, thou only I sent it to thee; thy sisters, do not mention it to them. The bundle which the wise bound, let a fool untie it".' The boy says, 'I am going now. Tomorrow do not mention me to thy sisters.'

The boy went in the night. He arrived at his master's in the bush. His master asks him, 'Didst thou do as I ordered thee?' The boy says, 'I did do so.'

The women at home, to whom the bundles were sent, Uoua the first kept the bundle in the box. Uoua the second kept it in the box. Uoua the third also, she kept it in the box. Uoua the fourth thought, saying, 'The bundle, that he sent me, saying, "let her open it", I will open it, that I see what is in it.'

She opened it; she sees the rats, that are in. She cleans them out; she shaves them. She puts them in pot; she cooks them. She sticks them on a spit; she sticks it in roof. She kept quiet. They live on some days; ten days.

Na Nzuá, who had gone hunting, comes; he is in the house of Uoua the eldest, saying, 'Bring the bundle that I sent thee.' She opens the box; takes out the bundle; she unties it. The rats are all rotten; they have become maggots.

The man goes out; he goes to Uoua the second, 'Bring the bundle that I sent thee.' The woman opens the box; she takes it out; she unties it. In it are all maggots.

The man goes out; goes to Uoua the third. Says, 'Bring the bundle that I sent thee.' The woman opens the box; she takes out the bundle; she unties it. In it are maggots only.

The man goes out; goes to Uoua the youngest, 'Bring the bundle that I sent thee.' The woman stands up; she takes off the spit from the roof. The rats are dried.

The man laughs. He goes outside; he calls the crowd of the people of the village. He says, 'You, gentlemen, I went a-hunting. I tied four bundles; I sent them to my wives, saying, "the bundle which the wise tied, let the fool untie it". I made ten days in the bush. Today I have come home, saying, "You, wives, bring the bundles that I sent you." They take out the bundles; those of the elder three are rotten; the bundle of the fourth, of the youngest, is dried. Her rats are these. The elder three are fools; they are not intelligent. I will marry the youngest.' The elder three went away.

This brought about the saying: 'Elder and younger shall not marry one man.' Because the youngest took from her elder the man, because of her shrewdness.

Thus far we heard it. Finished.

8

Six Nyanga Texts

The following texts were collected in the field and translated from the Nyanga by Professor D. Biebuyck, formerly of Lovanium University, Congo Republic.

The Nyanga inhabit the forest region of north-western Kivu Province in the Congo Republic. They are a small, but culturally very rich, patrilineal group, who subsist mainly by hunting and growing bananas.

The oral prose tradition is rich and varied, there being a wide range of stories, legends, epic songs, proverbs, riddles, and prayers. The texts presented here belong to the *mushinga* category, that is to say they are recited and not sung as are *uwano*. The majority of men and women know some *mishinga*, while only a few people know *uwano*.

I

Two men went to trap in the forest. While they were trapping, one of them killed a young wild pig. They went to the village; said to one another, 'If we lay this young pig aside (which is our first kill), then our traps will fail to kill; and so the headman and

others will they not hear about that in the village?' The other
one, he also said to his companion, 'When we have finished
eating this small pig there in the forest, the teeth of the pig
cannot be hidden, will the village headman not hear?' They
came to a decision to eat the young pig. They said, 'As we are
here, both of us, there is no one who will take the news to the
village, so our traps will not become "not-killing anything." They
took the small pig, cut it into pieces: the two men shared it.
After they had set their traps again and had finished eating the
animal they went up to the village.

Two days passed; they are in the village. One of them got up
(early) to sit round the fire in the men's hut, where his companions are. He was giving other news, and there they are,
laughing, while sitting round the fire. And he who has remained
in the house sleeping, he got up and went to the place where his
companion is. He arrived there; they are laughing. He said to
his companion, 'You, what news are you telling here, not that
of the small pig we ate in the forest?' All his companions said
to him, 'Look! you have eaten a young pig in the forest!' His
companion told him, 'You are shaming yourself, for I have
been telling other news and there you are appearing and re-
vealing (the secret of) the small pig, saying that we have hidden
it and have eaten it in the forest.'

All the men, together with the headman, finished hearing
this news of the hidden thing.

2

There was a man; he had begotten seven children. Their
names were Yangara, all of them together, all had this same
name and their father also was Yangara. Yangara said to his
children: 'Because you quarrel with one another about this
name Yangara, you all go to the forest to kill a buffalo, then
you will be able to take the name of Yangara.'

All these, all together they went to the forest. They went to
run across the buffaloes' path. The elder (brother) asked his
brothers saying, 'What are we going to do?' The one who
follows at his back said to their elder, 'You will know how we
will act, you will find the teaching that will make known to us
(how) to kill this buffalo, because you are Yangara as my
father is also.' The elder set his foot on the ground; dug out a

trench. And the one who follows him said to him, 'You have not covered the ditch.' The third one said to them, 'Your brainpower is useless'; he took a leaf, covered (the trench) with it there. After some days had passed, there died in this ditch a buffalo. The fourth Yangara tied it up; took it out. In order to carry it, Yangara the fourth took a knife, and cut the animal; cut it into pieces, just pieces. The fifth one wrapped it; wrapped it up, and carried it to the village: he too was up to that knowledge. Also the sixth one carried it on his back, laid it down at his father's; he also was Yangara. Their father inquired about all their knowledge: to dig, to cover, to take the animal out of the trench, to carry it, to cut it into pieces, to wrap it up in bundles.

Their younger (brother) remained behind (i.e. was left) among them, the last-born, he sought a piece of wood and beat it saying, 'He who has died may he rise again!' The buffalo stood up, went his way to the forest from where it had come. This child told his father, saying that he had sent the buffalo back to the forest because it was (too) small to share out to all the people; therefore he found out how to send it back. His father said to him, 'You also have not done wrong.' All of them he called by the name Yangara.

3

There was a man; he begot a boy. This man became sick of an illness. When he was about to die, he asked his child, saying, 'When I will have finished dying, what will you do?' He said to him that he did not know. He said to him, 'When he dies you will cut off the little finger, that little finger will save you; when he has finished dying, that little finger you will put it near the door, you will dig it in there.' Then his father died; he cut off his finger, and dug out a grave in the middle of the village ground.

When a month had passed after his father had died, he woke up early, saw in the village houses had grown up like crops around where he was. He became chief; all the inhabitants were bringing him tribute.

While they were sitting thus with joy, his wife questioned him. And there where the finger had been dug in, there was sprouting a *musae*-tree. She asked her husband saying, 'We were poor

and now we are rich, from where does it come our richness?'
When she got tired with her husband, he went to tell her about
the secret counsel which had been left to him by his father,
what he had been asked to do and how he had put that little
finger in the grave. When his wife had heard this news—just
imagine, she was being adulterous with a man—she gave the
news to her lover, all the news, what her husband had done and
why he had become chief.

In the early morning he assembled all his people; they came,
asked him why this tree was staying here, that such a tree was
not in the middle of the village. He failed to give them a reply,
he said that this tree was self-grown. She appeared there, his
sweetheart, his wife, revealed everything of how this tree had
grown. This chief lost his chief's status.

4

There was a woman, she gives birth to two children; the first-
born is Bureo and the other one is Murero. Their mother is
Nyabureo.

His mother said to Bureo as she was going to the forest,
'When you see the child is crying, cook him dry bananas.'
After his mother had gone to the forest, there, where Bureo has
remained, the child begins to cry. He took it, killed it, cooked it
with the dry bananas, saying his mother had told him when the
child begins crying to cook it with bananas. He cooked it,
having finished killing him. His mother came back, asked
Bureo, saying, 'Where is your younger brother?' He replied
that she had said to him that when the child cries he should
cook it with bananas; he had finished cooking it.

His mother, when she saw that she does not see her child, sang:

> 'Bureo, stupid fellow (lit. 'Father', 'venereal disease'),
> Has eaten my child.
> Catch for me Bureo
> He has eaten my child
> Catch for me Bureo
> He has eaten it with bananas
> Catch for me Bureo.'

While she was chasing him here and there (to and fro) to kill
him, he escaped.

There where he escaped, he met women from God's place (*il rencontra des femmes de chez Dieu*); they showed him the way. There where he went he met tree-clearers felling trees. They said to him, 'What are you fleeing for?' He said to them that he was fleeing from the women who say that he had revealed their secret and that the secret of women is not to be disclosed.

There where his mother was left, she sang:

> 'Catch for me Bureo,
> He has eaten my child
> He has eaten it with bananas.'

He passed beyond the tree-clearers; he came out near the river there where water is drawn. He met his paternal aunt (lit. 'female father'); his paternal aunt drew water after she had put Bureo in the jar. When she had arrived at (the house of) Kirimu (Monster), her husband the Monster Shebeni Muesa told his wife to give him water; she gave it to him. When he had tasted from it, he said that the water smelt like man. The Monster drank the water of another jar. After he had finished drinking that water, he got up (to go). This paternal aunt took the child away, put it on a heap of dirt, showed him the road that is leading to his maternal uncles, the Bats. There where he had gone to his maternal uncles, they took Bureo, forged him, sang:

> 'Bureo has refused the forge
> The forge is this one
> I am forging the sororal nephew
> The forge is this one.'

After they had finished forging him, the wanderer went, being called by the Monster Shebeni Muesa. He turned up at (the house of) the Monster. This one said to him that there, at his house, no other man arrives who is shaved with a razor. He told him, 'Let us go to Misukuubira, where comes out the dew of fire.' There they meet early, to fight with one another, to rush headlong one against the other. Bureo told him, 'We will go to Misukuubira when we have finished gambling.' He sang:

> 'He is gambling with Monster
> May his gambling beat him!'

They cast the dice (shells) one on the other; Bureo hit all the Monster's things. After he had been completely beaten, he told the child: that they should go to Misukuubira, both of them.

They set out to there, the child sang, 'We go with Shebeni to Misukuubira.'

They arrived there; Shebeni Muesa died there.

The child returned with the trophy of the Monster to show its paternal aunt that Shebeni Muesa is dead.

This Bureo went with fame; he was strong in the village of Monster Shebeni Muesa.

5

Sun and Rain started an argument with one another.

A young Monkey had begotten a daughter in another village. Rain arrived there, looking for this young girl. After he had arrived there, he talked to Monkey about his daughter. The father of the girl refused. After Rain has received this answer, he returned without anything and covered with shame.

When Sun had seen that Rain failed to get the girl, he, Sun, arrived there, asked for the girl, got her, and so became son-in-law of Monkey. War (danger) arrived, pursued Monkey. This war killed Monkey's wife and all his children, and he also had finished fleeing. There, where Monkey had fled, he shouted, 'You, Sun, because of the way you shone therefore I lose a lot of people.'

One day again, they hunted and hunted at Monkey's place. Rain also fell. They left him above, he had finished climbing up into the trees. Rain did not stop, it fell very hard. The hunters went home because of too much rain. After Rain has finished falling and Monkey has been saved, he (Rain) came to where he was and told him, 'You have given your daughter to Sun, saying he can save you, but I here have saved you and this although you have denied me your daughter.'

After he had thus been saved by Rain, Monkey took away his daughter from Sun, gave her to Rain because he had saved him. Rain went home with the daughter of Monkey where before he had been refusing her. His strength and his strong intelligence, it is because of that that he got her.

6

Isimbasimba and Ntanga made blood-brotherhood. Both are with their fathers and their mothers, together, all of them. One day, Ntanga's father became ill. Isimbasimba told his friend, 'Medicine can cure your father, it is good to search for the bark of a *musoke*-tree, you will tie it fast to the belly; it's like a belt that you will tie around your father's belly, but strong people should tie it, not people who have no strength.' He took the bark of a *musoke*-tree, fastened it to the belly firmly, saying, 'As long as your father has not recovered, you will not remove this belt from around his belly.'

Days have passed; his father was cured. When they saw his father had completely recovered they untied the belt. Ntanga's body went up, then sank down, in the middle there remained nothing. Ntanga had said much wrong about his friend, saying his friend had made him pass through amazing things so that he becomes a cripple.

When days have passed, Isimbasimba's father became ill; he sent a messenger to Ntanga. He asked him to show him a medicine, as his father had become ill. Ntanga arrived at the end of the village; they are beginning to weep as the father of his companion is already dead. He says, go, first, and bite on a small piece of wood that he may die leaving to you a good word. He went to bite on a small piece of wood: Ntanga said, 'Bite hard; hold on strongly, don't let it go.' Isimbasimba, his father died, and he is still (busy) on that small piece of wood; there where he bit on it he also died there.

These two men outdid one another in amazing things in this way.

9

Onecike

This and the following text were collected in the field and translated into French from the Tetela by J. Jacobs with the collaboration of W. A. A. Wilson in the preparation of the English version. *Onecike* was first published in an article 'Principes généraux de la nouvelle orthographe otetela-kikusu (Kasai–Kivu)', J. Jacobs (with the collaboration of B. Omeonga and H. Lukale), *Kongo-Overzee*, vol. xxv, 1959.

The Tetela are an important Bantu-speaking people of the Central Congo.

THERE was a man who had a child; when he had had this child and he had reached the age of about seven, his mother died. When his mother died, the child was left alone with his father. After he had lived with him for some time, his father also died. The child was left homeless and alone; there was no one in his father's family and no one in his mother's family, nor even any friend of his father's to take care of him. So the child was alone, and as yet was not strong enough to fend for himself. He began to have many jiggers; he had some in his feet, and even right up to his knees. His body was covered with scabies and his head with ringworm. He found it difficult to get any food. After thinking things over for a long time, Onecike[1] felt he could not remain like this any longer, and said to himself, 'Let us go and find a protector. But where? And if anyone tries to harm me, what will be, will be.'

Onecike set off at random. He walked a very long time and suddenly heard the noise of a smithy. He said to himself, 'Maybe there is someone there.'

Onecike went to the place where the noise was coming from. He came near the smithy and found the smith at work.

He entered the shed and sat down. 'Smith,' he said, 'I have come to you because I want to blow the bellows in your smithy.' The smith replied, 'That is all right with me.' The smith adopted the child and entrusted him to his senior wife. Onecike was first of all given the bellows to blow, and in return the smith took him under his care. The child's health improved, although he was only given *ma*[2] crusts to eat.

Onecike said to the smith, 'Mbapa,[3] make me a fish-hook so that I can go to the river to catch some fish.' The smith made him a fish-hook and gave it to him. Onecike got his fishing-rod ready, and one day went to fish in the river and caught many fish. Onecike came back to the village with the fish, went to the woman to whom he had been entrusted and gave them to her. The woman took the fish and prepared them. Having cooked them, all she put by for him was the heads and some *ma* crusts. Onecike took this food, but when he saw it he was disappointed and exclaimed, 'Now I brought this fish, and I am only getting the heads. But what can I do about it?' Onecike ate the *ma* crusts and the fish-heads.

Another day Onecike went fishing again, and caught even

---

[1] 'Onecike' = 'orphan, homeless child'.
[2] 'Ma' = food made with rice or millet.
[3] 'Mbapa, mpapa' = form of address for certain male relatives and other adults.

more fish than the first time. He brought the fish back to the village and gave it to his adoptive mother. She prepared it and once again gave him fish-heads and *ma* crusts. Onecike's heart overflowed with bitterness.

Another day, on his way to fish he was grumbling and saying to himself, 'Here I am, going off again for nothing, for of the fish I bring back each time they only leave me the heads, while the others eat the tasty part.' He came near the river, took his hook and threw it in the water, and pulled out a fish. Onecike threw in his hook again and this time it remained caught on a tree trunk. However hard he pulled, the hook did not come off. Onecike said to himself, 'Maybe it is a fish holding back my hook.' But no, it was indeed a tree trunk the hook was caught on. He said, 'Now that hook is lost, how shall I dare go back to my master?' He pondered, 'If I am to be the victim of the wild beasts which infest the waters, so be it, for I cannot leave someone else's fish-hook in the water and go back empty-handed to a village where I am only a stranger.' He dived in and swam along the fishing-line to where the hook was caught.

When he got to the bottom of the water, he was very surprised to find himself in a very crowded village. He saw in front of him his father and mother who had died long ago, and were now welcoming him warmly. The whole village was celebrating. They walked on ahead of Onecike and showed him to a house that was amply stocked with wealth of all kinds; in that house there was a large number of rooms.

His parents showed Onecike a door which they forbade him to open so long as he lived in that house. They said to him, 'You can enter every room, all their riches will be yours, but do not cross the threshhold of the forbidden door.' Onecike agreed. In the underground village (actually under the river-bed) there was soon no one who recognized him as the poor little orphan. He lived in plenty and only dressed in fine clothes. He was living in a chief's big village. He lived there many years, but finally was seized with dissatisfaction.

One evening he said, 'Now I am rich, I am living in a big village, where I am staying with my father and mother who died long ago, yet I am forever haunted by the longing to open the door of that little room. I cannot resist much longer; I shall end by opening that room, and nothing will happen when I do.'

One day when these same thoughts were troubling him he went to the room and opened the door. When he had entered, far from finding himself in the room he had imagined, he was carried back to the moment when his fish-hook had been caught on the tree-trunk. Once again he was dressed in rags, and covered with scabies, ringworm, and jiggers. All these misfortunes which had left him in the underground village where he was with his father and mother, all befell him again. Onecike at the river's edge looked in vain about him for the big, populous village, the big house, the wealth and the belongings he had enjoyed. 'What a plight I am in; I can no longer go back to the village I left such a long time ago.' The hook was still firmly caught on the tree. He said to himself, 'There is nothing for it but to dive back into the water and go back there.' He dived in and disappeared, and never again reached the world of his ancestors.

You see how a fool lost his happiness because he wanted to see what should have remained hidden from him.

So ends my story.

10

How the Tortoise took the Bees' Drums

See introductory note to Text 9.

ONE day all the animals had begun to carve dancing drums. The bees too had carved theirs. Having finished making their drums, the animals wanted to play them, but they only produced a dull sound. When the bees tried out their drums they gave a very clear note and the sound carried a very long way.

Because of this the other animals were most vexed and determined to take the bees' drums.

The elephant then said, 'Let me go; I will go first and see, and take their drums from them.' When the elephant reached the bees and tried to take their drums they fell on him and stung and stung him. The elephant fled right away. When he got back to the other animals he said, 'You have no idea how it hurts; no one will ever be able to take the bees' drums from them.'

The animals drove him away scornfully, saying, 'How so,

great lord of the forest? We sent you, thinking you were the king of all the animals, and so strong, yet you have ended up as a coward.'

The wild pig then said, 'Let me go; I have long teeth, I will certainly manage to get the drums.' He went off and reached the bees' place, but suffered the same fate as the elephant. As he got back to the other animals he said, 'You have no idea how it hurts; no one will ever be able to take the bees' drums.' The animals drove him away scornfully.

The animals went one after the other to the bees, but all suffered the same fate and were stung by the bees.

Finally the tortoise came up and said, 'Let me go; I will manage it.' The animals cried mockingly, 'You useless little fellow, with your little legs and slow gait! What would you go and do at the bees' place? How can you succeed where strong animals have failed?

The tortoise set off and went on and on till he reached the bees' place. They happened to be busy playing their drums, which gave clear loud notes. The tortoise caught them unawares and took a drum here and a drum there, and hoisted them on his shoulders.

Seeing this, the bees began to sing, 'O all you bees, with your dangerous stings, see, the drums are going, the drums are going.' The bees fell on the tortoise, and stung and stung him, but he said, 'All that is quite useless, my friends! I am in my shell.'

The tortoise got right away with the drums. When he returned to his friends, they seized the drums and played and played them, saying to one another, 'This is how we would have liked our drums to sound.'

The animals enjoyed the sound and the sweet rhythms and began to dance. The tortoise wanted to join with them in their dance, but the animals pushed him aside, crying, 'You useless little fellow! Do you want to dance to the music of our drums with your little legs? Clear off!'

The tortoise said bitterly, 'How so? We have been living in the same village. You others did not manage to go and fetch the bees' drums; I went, and succeeded, and now you drive me away, saying I have little legs and I cannot dance.'

The sun set, and the sun rose again. The animals had gone to the forest, and the tortoise had stayed at home. In the shelter

where the animals usually met a fire was burning; in the
tortoise's home, too, a fire was burning. The tortoise was
sitting quietly, wondering how to get his own back.

The tortoise went to the animals' shelter, made a bag of
banana leaves, filled it with water, and hung it over the fire
that was burning in the shelter; then the tortoise went home.

It began to rain. The animals came back from the forest and
settled down in the shelter, by the fire. As they were chatting,
suddenly one of them noticed the bag hanging from the roof of
the shelter. They wanted to know what was in it, so one of them
took a spear, thrust at the bag and pierced it; the water inside it
poured out over the fire and quenched it completely.

That was how the tortoise got his own back. Now, when he
goes walking with his slow gait, you may know that he has a fire
burning at home. The other animals, ever since that happened
to them, have never had a fire.

11

Kaayowa

Originally written in Luba in the periodical *Nkuruse* in 1926
by an unknown author, this English version has been prepared by the late C. de Goede of Nijmegen, Holland.

The Luba-Kasai are divided into many tribes, one being the Bakwa
Diisho(i). This is divided into many clans, including the BaYomba,
who live in the south (Kaayowa's clan); the Bakwa Cimuna,[1] who
live in the north (Kaayowa's first husband, Mwamba wa Kajaakulu,
belonged to a subdivision of this group); and the Beena Cimungu,
who also live in the south (to whom Kaayowa subsequently fled, and
amongst whom she remained).

The text tells of a war which breaks out between clans of the Bakwa
Diisho tribe because of a woman. At first the Bakwa Cimuna win,
thereafter the Beena Cimungu. The Bakwa Cimuna call in the
Bakwa Nsumpi, and the Beena Cimungu invoke the help of the
Bakwanga. Later on the Bakwanga turn against the Beena Cimungu,
who had called them in, so then Ciaba, chief of the Beena Cimungu,
calls in the Bakwa Kalonji.

I

KAAYOWA was a Yombo; she had gone with her parents to
live with the Cimungu. Her uncles on her father's side also had

_____
[1] The 'c' is pronounced as the English 'ch'.

settled down with the Cimungu. At that time Kaayowa was a
little girl. When she had grown into a beautiful woman, a
young man of the Cimuna, sprung from the clan of the Kadima,
fell in love with her and he married her. Then she lived with her
Kadima husband, who was named Muamba ua Kajuukulu.
However, after some time she left him and went back to the
Cimungu. She settled down in Kamba, a village which belonged to the clan of the Kaninda. There she set up house for
a man called Mubikaayi ua Kapumbe. Mubikaayi, seeing her
beauty, tasting her good cooking, and overcome by her love-
liness, said to her, 'Kaayowa, you are my wife.' Kaayowa complied with him and loved him very much. But she told him, 'I
was already married to a Cimuna. My husband lives in the
village of the Cimuna, he will come to get me.' Her informant
replied, 'No, my dear, you cannot go back to the Cimuna.' Her
Cimuna husband went in search of her without finding her.
When he went through all the villages inquiring after Kaayowa
he was told his wife lived with the Cimungu and she had married another man. Having arrived at his parents-in-law they
told him they did not approve of the second marriage of their
daughter; Kaayowa was his wife, she should go back to him.
Muamba ua Kajuukulu went to the Cimungu to claim his wife.
However, he risked getting beaten up. The Cimungu said, 'Let
us give him a dressing down.' Our man, not wanting to die
without reason, fled.

2

Back in his village, Muamba ua Kajuukulu talked it over with
his friends. His family and friends, hearing what had happened,
said, 'The Cimungu called us silly geese.' That night they
played the drums. And in this way the news was communicated
to all Cimuna. The day after, the Cimuna came down from
every nook and corner of the country. They agreed unanimously
and said, 'This night we shall claim the lawful wife of Muamba
ua Kajuukulu by drum and as the night is over we shall hear
what the Cimungu chiefs will answer.' When it got dark they
went to sleep and at early dawn the Nkongolo chief took the
drums and began playing them. He placed the Cimungu chiefs
in possession of all the facts. He posted up Kabonzo ua Ciabo-
Matala-Makanga, Ciaba Mulombo, and Nkutula. However,

the Cimungu chiefs did not pay attention at all to the news Nkongolo posted to them by the drums. Although they understood the news very well they acted as if everything in the garden was rosy. They answered with disdain. Hearing this, the Cimuna got very angry. They deliberated and communicated to each other that war was declared. One morning they played the drums and challenged the Cimungu. The drums told the Cimungu, 'We take pleasure in putting up a fighting-line on this beautiful morning.' The Cimungu, being told the war was on, pretended to have foreseen this fact. They uttered unanimous shouts as if they had slept in the same house.

3

The day after, chief Nkongolo opened the hostilities and they marched against the Cimungu. The events developed as follows. The neighbouring Cimungu, spotting the warriors, used their drums to post their clansmen what was was on. The Cimuna climbing the mountain, and the Cimungu coming down, collided, and there was a long battle. On both sides many warriors died heroes. But the Cimuna conquered the Cimungu. They set the houses on fire and also the nearest villages. They penetrated far into the country of the Cimungu. When all Cimungu were packed together inland they planned not to give any more ground. The Cimuna and the Cimungu killed each other for a long time. A thrown lance wounded the son of the chief of the Cimuna. This son was called Mukanie Cisanga. He was a war hero. When he fell to the ground the Cimungu said, 'We shall kill him, we shall behead him.' The worthy reply of the Cimuna was, 'Our hero may not stay behind on the field of honour without his head.' They did not fight any longer. The shields clashed in the air. The Cimuna were the stronger. They left the battlefield taking along Makanie Cisanga. However, the Cimungu pursued them for a long time and finally they gained the victory over the Cimuna. They killed and beheaded Mabika ua Musenga, a hero of the Cimuna, well known to all the people of the Diisho tribe. The Cimuna took to flight and they went back to their village. Having buried their dead and after a good night's rest they called up their brothers the Mbuuyu and they joined forces. Next they appealed to the Nsumpi and all together they marched again against the Cimungu. They slaughtered a great many and set so many houses on fire that the Cimungu took to their heels. Their villages remained deserted and destroyed behind.

In this the commoners were not included but only the nobles, the heroes, the great commanders or the sons of chiefs. When they claimed the woman Kaayowa, the Cimungu would not hand her over. Their only answer was, 'Let us immediately make away with these noisy warriors.' The Cimuna and the Mbuuyu fled the region taking along Kaayowa.

4

Ciabu Mulombo gathered soil and put it in a basket. He brought it to Muteeba ua Citaka, the chief of the Kwanga. He spoke to him as follows, 'I am a man of the same rank as you are, I bring you this soil of the Diisho tribe. I have come to ask you for warriors. People of the same tribe set my clan's houses on fire and killed many of my warriors. If your forces are strong, then set all the houses of my enemies on fire. Kill them and take hold of their territory.' Muteeba ua Mpungue Citaka, hearing the news, took the drums and put them on his legs and called up all the Kwanga. The Kwanga flocked together. He told them, 'Ciaba Mulombo of the Diisho tribe brought this soil to us people. He has come to ask for warriors. The men of his tribe (the Cimungu and the Cimuna also belong to the powerful tribe of the Diisho) killed and wounded his subjects and even called in the aid of the Nsumpi, who defeated his force on his own ground.' The Kwanga, hearing that, shouted, 'We want to fight this war; as for the soil they have brought you, the Kwanga will not fail.' Unanimously they declared war. The day after, the warriors took the field and marched against the Diisho. After a long journey they reached the environs of Diisholand and they made a halt in the bush. The nearest relations of the Diisho who were among the Kwanga went to their relatives in secret and informed them the day after it would be war. Thus the Diisho knew what they might expect. The spies of the Diisho tribe traced what was going on in the bush and they informed their chiefs. When the Kwanga marched onward they clashed with the Diisho warriors. It was a big battle. There were warriors killed, many others got wounded. However, the attack of the Kwanga crushed the resistance of the Diisho. The

Diisho were conquered, their houses were set on fire, and their possessions were appropriated. Most of the warriors of the Diisho army were Cimuna and Mbuuyu. The Kazaadi, who lived among them, surrounded them. The Kwanga, setting the houses of the Cimuna and those of the Mbuuyu on fire, killed many commoners and drove the others away from their villages.

5

When the Kwanga had returned to Ciaba Mulombo, who had called in their assistance, they attacked his people, and they put them to flight, killing many of them, and setting their houses on fire. When Ciaba Mulombo noticed this he got angry and said, 'The Kwanga are mistaken. They have come to kill my own people who had called them in to their aid.' He filled another basket with soil and brought it to Mutombo Kaci. He asked him for warriors in order that the Kalonji would kill the Kwanga. Mutombo Kaci on his part assembled his forces and he fought the Kwanga. Many noblemen perished on the battlefield. The corpses lay piled up. The Kalonji were immediately defeated. However, at another battle the Kalonji shattered the Kwanga; they killed a great many of them and they put them to flight. Mutombo Kaci commanded his warriors, 'Don't kill those hounds, catch them alive.' After this order was accomplished the Kalonji occupied the territory; they made their wives and children come over and they settled down.

6

The chief warrior Ciaba Mulombo had lost many of his warriors in the battles. Numerous were the dead of the whole Diisho tribe. Plenty of Nsumpi heroes whom the Cimuna had called in, bit the dust. The warriors of the Kalonji tribe, whom the Cimungu had sent for at long last, also counted many dead. Then the noblemen began taking stock. The Cimungu said, 'Many of our warriors got killed! Moreover we lost our own territory in this affair! And that all for the sake of one woman, Kaayowa. So now must we end this war.' The elderly people put Ciaba Mulombo in the wrong and they said to him, 'Would you have sent back Kaayowa to the Cimuna in the beginning before all this trouble started; would that have made worse this

affair?' They spoke very angrily. They continued, 'Well! Must
we all die?! Do you withdraw or what else are you up to?'
Ciaba Mulombo did not know what to answer. When the noblemen spoke that way the situation was critical, the country was
in chaos, the war had exterminated most of the *élite*. The best
warriors of the Diisho tribe, of the Kwanga, the Nsumpi and the
Kalonji had been killed. The dispute was so knotty that nobody was able to solve the problem. On the land itself the
provisions had been destroyed by the military operations. The
men were tongue-tied.

7

All the clans of the Diisho tribe argued the same way with the
high-ranking chiefs, the dignitaries of the villages, and the
chiefs of war. All of them resolved on a course of action:
Kaayowa must be hanged. They asked Ciaba, who had un-
chained the war, 'You who took Kaayowa under your protection, you who gave up a part of our country to the Kwanga and
another part to the Kalonji; you, Ciaba Mulombo, tell us:
Where can we get the cassava, where the corn, where the
millet? Where are the beans? Where are the sweet potatoes?
Tell us what is your advice.' Then Kabeya Mvuangala, the
mightiest chief of the Diisho tribe, stood up and he said in a
loud voice, 'You chief Mayembe 'a Mbuuyu, you and your
subjects the Cimungu must fetch the woman called Kaayowa,
and we shall turn her over to Konji, the chief of this territory,
this way recouping the affliction caused to him. Further we
shall call a general meeting and we will come to an agreement.
After that we shall smoke the peace-pipe with the Kwanga.'

Kayembe 'a Mbuuyu accepted the proposal. They caught
Kaayowa and collected goats to deliver them to the chiefs.

8

Kaayowa was seven months advanced in pregnancy. They
brought her to Konji, the chief of the Cimuna. The chiefs took
possession of the goats. When Kaayowa fell into the hands of
the Diisho tribe all of them shouted unanimously, 'May
Kaayowa die in the presence of all the women and children.
May the goats, the dogs, the chickens, the toads, and all insects

open their eyes to see how Kaayowa dies.' The chiefs fired off speeches in which they praised the bravery of their war-chiefs. There was a mighty commander called Muuka-Kaninda ua Diulu; Kaayowa was handed over to him. The men, women, and children began reproaching Kaayowa, 'You were married, the dowry was given to your family. Why did you leave your husband and why did you bring the dispute on your country? The husbands of other women died because of you, those women have no men any more to live with. You are a criminal. The day has come when you must die with your crime. Sink with your crime as the water sinks.' They set up a roar, they cried 'Away with the crime! Away with the criminal! Who will put an end to the crime and the criminal!' They made Kaayowa mount the scaffold and they put a rope around her neck. Then Kaayowa said in a loud voice that she did not want to die without having said a word. 'You men will see me die, may this be a lesson to you, never marry a woman who has already been married. Everyone who marries that way may he or she also be hanged!' When they took away the pedestal she fell down and died. They finished her with the sword, and they cut her into pieces. Muuka Kaninda cut open her womb and delivered the unborn child. He attached it to a staff and went away, showing it to the people in the market-places.

Kaayowa did not find anyone to bury her. She was treated in an undignified way.

9

And this is the way things on this earth go. The dog that eats a parrot will also die with the parrot. Kaayowa of the Yombo left behind fame without peer. It was because of her many people faded out of this territory. She obtained quite a reputation as well with the men as with the women. The quarrel over one woman caused the ruin of many men in the villages and wrecked the territory of all the clans which were involved in the dispute.

12

Lake Munkamba

This mythological account of the origin of Lake Munkamba
originally appeared in Luba in the periodical *Nkuruse* in 1927.
This English version has been prepared by the late C. de
Goede of Nijmegen, Holland.

Lake Munkamba is situated about 62 miles east-north-east of Lulua-bourg, in the Kasai. The lake is more than 15 miles in circumfer-ence, lies in a depression, and water flows neither into nor out of it. It is situated in the most southern part of the territory of the Bakwa Luntu, and forms the border between them and the Luba and Bena Luluwa. A conference was held, as recently as 1960, by the chiefs of the Kasai to try to find a solution for the war between the Bena Luluwa and the Luba. The Bakwa Luntu, who live in the Dimbe-lenge area, number about 100,000, and were often known as the Bena Konji (*les Koshes*), both officially and elsewhere. Though unjust, the name has a historical justification. Konji was the chief of the Bakwa Fika, one of their small clans, who became a leader of a rebel movement against the Government, in this way becoming a celebrity. After Konji's death in prison, the label persisted.

From the point of view of social structure the Bakwa Luntu are divided into thirty-two patrilineal clans. All these claim to be descended from a common ancestor, Luntu. They are most closely linked with the Bena Luluwa in language, diet, and housing, the language being a straightforward dialect of Luba.

MY dear Friends, all of you nice people will be very much interested to hear something about the origin of the famous Lake Munkamba in the Congo. Well, my friends, relax, sit down in your easy chair and I shall tell you the story. The so-called Lake Munkamba came into existence by the magical power of the witches. If you don't believe me go to the Congo and ask my coloured friends at Lake Munkamba; they will certainly tell you. The region where you will find Lake Munkamba is called Citamba. The people who lived there in the old days were called the Bakua-Cishimbula; those people, who were quiet men and women rather than warriors, who loved to fish, to hunt, to take care of the needs of a well-ordered society in their pleasant village, had come from the Central Congo. These Bakua-Cishimbula conceived a great plan. They planned to make themselves a safe haven of refuge. You might put the question to me: why would these nice men and women build themselves a safe haven of refuge? To tell you the truth this would be a long story; to make it short the Bakua-Cishimbula lived always in fear of neighbouring clans, who were jealous of their prosperous way of living. And since these good people lived in open country they lacked the means to hide themselves from their enemies, or to put up a good defence. So they lived day by day in fear of getting killed by bad people. And so it happened they looked for a way of escape. And what better could they do than to make themselves a road to heaven to sit in the lap of Almighty God and to have a good hiding-place. But how could that be realized? They called a great meeting and it was on that meeting they undertook the commission to build a gigantic road to heaven. For months they went to a far-away forest and cut down kingly trees and brought them over to their field. Then they started to tie them together and to put them upwards. But, alas, what happened? When they had reached the first clouds the trees below collapsed under the heavy weight of the trees at the top and the mighty fortress of trees came down to the earth. No need to tell you friends doomsday seemed to be at hand. Those giants of the forest had a terrible ending and with them the good Bakua-Cishimbula, a big whirlpool had suddenly come into being, and the giants and the people of the above-mentioned village were overpowered by the whirlpool which only in later days became a quiet lake.

The above-mentioned stretch of country—nowadays only water is left—was occupied by the Bakua-Cishimbula. In those days only pools could be found, which were scattered all over the region up to Katende. It was at those pools the women came to draw their water and to soak the cassava. Their children used to play with calabashes. In between their playing they pressed their parents, squeezing the wild fruits between their fingers saying, 'Mama, I am so thirsty, please give me some water!' and, 'Papa, please give me some beer.' Their parents grumbled then, saying, 'Children, who asked you to nag that way? When you draw water from those pools on this field and you drink it and you die that is up to you.' However, the children did not cease to ask for water and they even got beaten. One day—it was just before noon—when most men and women had gone into the bush while others stayed home, the children started again their play, always singing, 'Mama give me water, Papa give me beer.' At noon they were still singing the same song, the *masusu* squeezed between their fingers. They had an argument with the earth, they beat the soil with their hands and kicked at it with their feet. Then they got tired and they laid down for a siesta. Suddenly they woke up with a start and, terrified, watched a wave of water which came roaring on and which fell upon the children. They jumped to their feet and began crying, they screamed, beating the hand on the mouth, 'Papa, we shall die, Papa, we shall die!' The most nimble ones, who were still outside the water, and those who were the biggest ran away as fast as they could without knowing where to go. The others got lost at the bottom of the water. When the adults who had stayed behind in the village went out to see what might have happened to the children the only thing they found was the water, which had even inundated a part of their village. The most cunning broke into a run and like the biggest children they escaped a certain death. The others watched the place or jumped into the water. Houses, trees, people, horses, chickens, everything was buried under the water. There was nothing left of the village. Only those who fled and those who were in the bush were saved. But the others were exterminated until the present day. When the villagers who had gone into the bush came back home they found nothing else but the water, which spread everywhere. They did not know where to go, they were shut in by water, which had absorbed their children, friends, and possessions. That is why there are tears. They parted immediately, they went to the south and they finally reached the lower regions.

And . . . the water remained for ever.

Our friends in the Congo know also another version about the origin of Lake Munkamba. The children of a friendly village had gone out to catch grasshoppers, namely the *nkupu* grasshoppers (these are the little ones) and the *bibeetu* grasshoppers (these are caught by beating them with a stick to which plaited palm fibres are attached). On their way to catch grasshoppers they ventured far off into the bush. It was an extremely hot day. They were very thirsty, their mouth was dry without any saliva. They looked for water, but in vain. Having come some distance in the bush they found ripe *masusu* (wild fruits which have a carmine colour). Those fruits grew there in such an abundance as they had never seen before. They gathered the *masusu* and filled their game-bags to the brim. Then they sat down with the *masusu* under a little tree, they opened the fruits and ate them. Others were squeezed to extract the juice from them. Having eaten them they were still thirsty. Then they began to sing, 'Mama give me water! Papa give me juice! Mama give me water! Papa give me juice!' Singing like that they stamped their feet. And since the silly water did not like their stamping on the soil it got born(?). After a shorter or longer period the children looked up and saw a dense fog coming over them, accompanied by a deafening noise which was heard everywhere. When they jumped up wondering where the buzzing came from they saw the threatening calamity which hung over them drawing near, the fog became denser and denser and flashes of lightning split it. While they were still squeezing the *masusu*, they had given themselves all sorts of names. Some of the kids called themselves the flying spiders, others the creeping snakes, there were also those who named themselves the rolling ripples (little curling waves), then there were some who gave themselves a name I cannot remember any more. When they observed the approaching forces of nature they separated. The flying spiders flew up and went back home. The creeping snakes crept away but the rolling ripples remained rolling on the soil not knowing where to go. The others climbed up into the trees. When the water invaded, it absorbed the ripples and those who were in the trees, it exterminated them completely until the days we are living in.

Those who went back home told the village all that had happened. When the parents of the drowned children heard the bad tidings their weeping was heard all over the village. And in this way, my dear friends, Lake Munkamba came into existence, namely, as a result of a children's game.

And so it happened, our informant says, that the lake had its origin.

The Ghosts

After the ceremonies of mourning the women and the others settled down near the lake. At that time the lake was rather

small. The women used to soak the cassava in it. The denizens
of the water, my dear friends, the water-ghosts, observing the
water get tainted, became very angry and rebuked the women.
During the night they rose from the water and went into the
houses scolding the women, saying, 'You women, leave this
region, you spoil our water, our bodies begin to smell badly and
besides you deprive us of the opportunity to warm ourselves in
the sun and you send away our objects.' Then the water went
away under the soil and, to chase away the people, it appeared
again in the village making channels like those of the termite
mounds on the fields and in the houses. When a man heard a
rumbling noise in his house he nosed around to discover a
channel. He took a palm nut and threw it into the water. The
sound it made convinced him the water was deep. He left
the house immediately and warned his neighbours, who left
the village as soon as possible. Concerning those who doubted
and who shammed deaf, all of them were dragged along by the
raging water into the lake in which they got buried for always.
Concerning the women who used to soak the cassava in the lake,
they found the cassava already spread out on the beach. Above
the cassava they found washed up pearls, table linen, blankets, and
other articles of luxury. They went back home very much upset
and told the people, 'We had gone to soak the cassava and we
found pearls, table linen, blankets, and other articles of luxury.'

Who put those things there? The next day, coming back to
the lake it was the same. Back home the women informed their
husbands. When there was no end to it the menfolk called a
meeting. When the meeting was over they told their wives, 'You
women go back to the lake and when you find those articles
again, tell those who put them down: "We do not want those
luxurious things, don't put them down any more, take them for
always, put them away." Since we live in a country without any
luxury and we are fought against day by day, you ought to
renounce them; were we to get hold of them would that mean
the end of the war? Those who have become strong and rich
would they not come to destroy us completely? "Please take
them away and never put them down again." In case they were
to ask you, "But what do you want then?" answer them: "The
only thing we want is the fish we need to eat *nshima*, we don't
want luxuries."' When the women went back to the lake they

followed the advice of their husbands. The water-ghosts answered them: 'Since you refused that luxury and only ask for fish, that also is all right. We will give you the fish you ask for. But ask your husbands about the sort of fish they want to catch. Do they prefer the *mende*, the *kaboobo*, the *cisaka-mamba*, the *cikele*, the *musangi*, or the *kakunda kaa bilombe*? Let them tell you what fish they want and come back to tell us.' The water-ghosts made the fish show their heads and tails and showed them to the women. Back in the village the women told their men. However, the men did not like these kinds of fish. Thus the men concluded the water-ghosts wanted to make things more difficult. That is the way of things known to the strong and the rich to make war on us people. They informed their women the only fish they wanted to catch was the *tukunda tua bilombe*, which they showed to them. In consequence the men themselves went to the lake to communicate their decision to the water-ghosts. Those answered them, 'That is all right with us, you will get what you want. But go to the eldest family in your village and get a naked man and a white goat, bring both of them to the lake and give them to us. We shall clear the border of the lake and you will catch the fish you are asking for.' The men went back to their village to fetch a naked man and a white goat. Having brought them to the lake they threw them into the water saying to the water-ghosts, 'We have acquitted ourselves in our task and have brought you both.' The water-ghosts welcomed them with joy, they thanked the villagers and beat their heads against their backs, which is a sign of approval, and told the villagers, 'You have done a great job.' Then they brought out a fish-trap, demonstrated it to the villagers, saying, 'You must use this instrument to catch the fish. Go then and plait similar nets and use those to trap the fish; you have chosen wisely rather than luxuries. Those who are buried in the lake, they too made and used the same fish-traps you have seen us demonstrating.' Those nets are shaped like sacks. The villagers planned to plait the nets and to catch fish with them. They would eat the fish and sell a part of them to buy with the proceeds chickens, crosses (copper coins in the form of a cross), and goats and even to marry women. May those fishes be blessed forever. We run our market at the edges of our lake, we call it the 'market of Munkamba'. There was no question any more of the luxuries which the water-ghosts offered to the villagers; those things had vanished for ever. There remained only shadows, which brought out the depth of the lake, the shadows of cows, horses, villages, red covers, rifles, flags, drawn-up soldiers, men and women, boys and girls, and other things on the bed of the lake. The shadow of white people who went among the others, some by bicycle, others on horseback, there were also on cowback and one could see people who remained standing in the lower part of the lake. Even our chiefs were visible in the deep water.[1]

They were decked out with colourful feathers. There were also drummers and clarion-blazers, who let resound their drums and clarions. As you hear, my friends, there are strange things happening down in the lake. And Lake Munkamba is still in the same place as it was in those old days. So those who think we are telling a nursery-tale, that is out of the question. When we fish in vain we offer our ancestors *nshima*, chickens, and goats. We planted *milemba* and *mimbu* trees at the edge of the lake and it is under the shadow of these trees we offer the water-ghosts *nshima*.

And this is the story of Lake Munkamba.

The Story of Uula Kabulua

The reason you hear so much talk about our lake is that there are found people in the lake who sing beautifully, who dance gracefully, who grind cassava, and who polish stones by rubbing them on other stones. There are even people who founded new villages down in the lake. For those who doubt all this I shall tell of a recent happening. Whenever you went to visit the lake you saw, undoubtedly, a palm tree on an island. There is also a shack on the same island. This shack has a lengthened roof. Well, does that shack not belong to Uula Kabulua? This Uula we are speaking of had a brother. One day the brothers went to the lake to catch fish. Having come to the lake they saw a string of palm nuts on the island. Uula swam the long distance to the island, and having reached the island he cut off the string of palm nuts. When he had finished the string fell on the ground,

---

[1] The water of the lake is very clear and colourful, it has mostly a deep green colour. On the bottom of it there are rocks. Those have such whimsical shapes one can imagine seeing all sorts of figures, as is the case with the clouds in the air.

began to roll and fell into the lake. According to people this lake originated from the crying of a woman who complained of her pots and jars.

Well, falling in the lake the string of palm nuts crashed into those jars, smashing them to pieces. The millet, corn, and flour was spread over the bottom of the lake. The wife's husband told Uula, 'Uula Kabulua what have you done? You cut off a string of palm nuts and this string has broken my wife's kitchen utensils. Well, at any cost you must buy jars and pots with millet, corn, and flour and bring them over to the lake. And when you cannot get those on the ordinary market then you must go to Kaaba-Kateya to buy those pots for my wife, if not I will start a palaver.' Uula went away and did as he was told; he bought those pots and brought them over to the island. The morning after, he swam back to the island and looked for the place where he had put the pots with the food the previous day.

He discovered everything was gone. The owners had come to pick them up. He heard somebody say, 'Uula Kabulua, you are a good chap, for you paid your debt and hereby I declare the palaver ended. My dear friend, come always to this lake to catch your fish to your heart's content. None of us water-people will ever disturb you and you will always make a nice haul.'

Uula used to fish there on the same place. One day he took his brother along. They had to swim across to the island. But what happened? The water-ghosts accompanied Uula's brother and at a given moment they began pulling his legs. The poor boy did not feel he could reach the island. He cried out, 'Uula, my brother, the water-ghosts will seize me and drag me along into the depths.' Uula swam as fast as he could, to rescue his brother. He used all possible means to get rid of the water-ghosts. They, feeling Uula was too strong for them told him, 'If you want to set your brother free, we will catch you and take you along.' Hearing this, Uula let loose his brother, who was taken along by the water-ghosts. When they had taken his brother along, Uula got angry and built himself a shack with a lengthened roof, so that his brother's ghost could stay there during the night. Uula remained always on the island and earned his living by fishing.

Nobody was ever able to reach the island but Uula, he who knows best the island. And this friends is the story of Uula.

13

The Story of the Four Miracle Workers

This and the two following stories were collected and translated from the Kamba by J. S. Mbiti, in the course of a
prolonged study of Kamba oral literature.

The Kamba, numbering almost three-quarters of a million, live in
the Machakos and Kitui districts of Kenya, south and east of
Nairobi, and with their closely related neighbours the Kikuyu make
up almost one-third of Kenya's African population.

Kamba stories are usually recited during the evening, indeed
Kamba go further and assert that *andŭ matiananĭaa mŭthenya, nŭndŭ
mbano ityĭ mŭyo mŭthenya* ('people don't tell one another stories during
the day, because they're not interesting in the daytime'). They may
be broadly divided into *ngewa*, stories with some element of prob-
ability, and *mbano*, wholly fictitious stories. In a note to these stories
Mr. Mbiti has pointed out that the division into *ngewa* and *mbano* is
by no means always clear-cut; some stories, like the first, being
largely probable but with elements of the wholly fictitious. The
second, by contrast, is largely fictitious, but still has some factual
elements in it.

THERE was a man whose wife bore him a son. He called his
name Musavili. But he was a very arrogant and stubborn boy.
Sometimes he refused to eat his food, and when his mother
bought him new clothes he refused to wear them, saying that
they were rubbish.

One day he said, 'Mother, go and buy me a flask and a hat.
I want to leave home and go away for ever.' So the mother
bought him a flask, and a very expensive hat worth eighty
shillings. When she gave them to him, he threw them away, and
said they were useless. His mother was disgusted, and she said
to him, 'Go where you want to go!' Then he left his home and
began to wander about in the forests.

One day, when he was walking in the plains, he saw a man

from a long distance. As he went nearer, he noticed that the man
was kneeling down, and had a gun in his hands. He said to the
man, 'Please do not shoot me.' The boy came to him, and
greeted him, 'How do you do?' He replied, 'How do you do,
Musavili?' The boy was surprised to find that the man knew his
name, and he said to him, 'So you know my name?'

'Yes, I do,' answered the man.

'And what are you doing here?' the boy inquired.

'I am waiting until some flies alight on top of Mount
Kilimanjaro, so I can shoot them!'

'How can you see a fly on top of such a high mountain?'

The man gave him power to see that far, and said to the boy,
'Now watch it.' He looked and saw a fly alight on the snow-
capped peak, and the man with the gun shot and broke its wing.
Then he said to the boy, 'Would you like to join me in my travel?'

'Yes, very much so,' answered the boy joyfully.

The man said, 'Very well. Let us be going then.' So they
went together. They travelled until the man said to the boy,
'Can you see that man over there?' He answered, 'Yes, I can.
But he seems to be standing on one leg only.' The man said,
'Let us get where he is.' They walked on until they came to the
man standing on one leg. They greeted him, 'How do you do?'
He replied, 'How do you do, Musavili and your friend?'

Musavili asked him, 'Why are you standing on one leg only?'

The man answered, 'If I should step on the ground with my
other leg, I would quickly move from here to another spot
immediately.' Musavili said, 'Try it and let us see.' The man
stepped on both feet, and no sooner did he do that than he
moved very fast and got back to the home of Musavili. It had
taken the boy two years to travel all that distance, but this man
did it within no time. The man came back and said to Musavili,
'If you want to, you may join me in my travel.' Musavili said he
would. The man said, 'Good. Let us be going then.'

When they had travelled a few more miles, this new man
said to Musavili, 'Do you see that person yonder there?' The
boy looked and said, 'Yes, I do. He looks like a man, but he
seems to be holding his nose.' The two men said, 'Let us get
where he is.' So they all went on until they reached the man who
was blocking his nostrils with a hand. They greeted him, saying,
'How do you do?' He replied, 'How do you do, Musavili and

your two friends?' Then Musavili asked him, 'Why have you
blocked your nostrils with your hand?' The man replied, 'If I
open my nostrils there will be a very strong wind!' Musavili
said, 'Open them a little bit and let us see what happens.' The
man did so, and suddenly a very strong wind began to blow,
knocked down all the trees around where they were. Musavili
immediately said to him, 'Please close your nostrils again.'
When he closed them the wind stopped blowing, and the man
said to Musavili, 'You may join me, if you want.' They all
travelled together, and then they saw another man holding
his wallet. Musavili was asked, 'Can you see that man?' He
answered, 'Yes, but he seems to be uprooting all the large trees
and squeezing them into his small wallet.' So they came to
where this other man was, and greeted him, 'How do you do,
man?' And he replied, 'How do you do Musavili and your
three friends?'

"What is your name?' Musavili asked him.

'My name is Mukua-miamba. The name means "one who
uproots *baobab* trees".'

'Will you uproot a few so we can see.'

He said, 'I have uprooted very many, and I have also
uprooted hills. Wait one moment, I will show them to you.'
Then he pulled out of his little wallet, one hill after another.
The man said to Musavili, 'You may join me if you want.'
Musavili said to Mukua-miamba, 'Yes, I will join you.' The
man replied, 'Very well, come, and let us be going.'

They went on until they came to the palace of the king of that
country. They were welcomed, and given beds to sleep on. The
following day there was a horse race at the palace, and
thousands of his subjects came to take part and to watch. The
king said that the winner would be given his beautiful daughter
to be his wife. The group that Musavili had joined was asked,
'Is there anyone among you who can take part in these com-
petitions?' Musavili answered, 'We shall try to find someone.'
All those that come to compete brought their own horses, and
so a horse was produced by the king, for Musavili and his group.
But Musavili told the king that although one of them was going
to take part, he would not use a horse but would merely run.
The judges said, 'Are you merely taking it as a joke?' Musavili
answered, 'No, we are serious.' The judges said, 'It is up to you.'

The whistle was blown, and the competitors began to run. After three hours, the man who walked on one leg decided now to run. He lowered his other leg and ran as fast as lightning. He reached the river, passing the other competitors on the way, and then turned to go back. But because he was so far ahead of the others, he stopped on the way back, and lay down and went to sleep. The king's daughter came, together with the other people, and they took his pitcher while he slept, and spilled all his water, and ran back to the palace. The other competitors now reached the river, and filled their pitchers, and began to gallop back to the palace.

The people waited anxiously at the palace, and began to ask one another, 'When will the winner get here?' Musavili heard it, and got very concerned. He asked the man who was shooting flies to look and find him, and when he did, Musavili asked him to shoot on his ear in order to wake him up. So the man was gently shot, and he woke up, only to find that his water had been spilled. Immediately he put down his other leg, got to the river again, filled up the pitcher and within two minutes he reached the palace. He passed all the other competitors on the way, and he became the winner. Everyone clapped his hands and congratulated him. When the other runners arrived, they were astonished to find him already there.

The king said to Musavili and his people, 'Tomorrow you will be given my daughter.' So they went to sleep, and at night, Musavili and the other men said to Mukua-miamba, 'Remove the house in which the princess is sleeping, and put it into your little wallet, and let us all go away. Remove the king's palace as well, and let us put it into the sea.' So the palace was removed and put into the sea, and both the king and his daughter and all those in the palace perished.

In the morning Musavili and his men saw about 30,000 soldiers following them, carrying guns. So they said to the man who kept his nostrils blocked, 'It is your turn now.' The man answered, 'Stand aside and see what happens.' So he opened his nostrils, and a very strong wind blew off all those soldiers into the sea, and they also drowned and perished.

These four men went with Musavili till they reached his home country, and they became kings. They are still ruling to this day.

14

Father and Son, Mother and Daughter

See introductory note to Text 13.

THERE is one story which my friend told me. That story was very interesting and amazing. It was about a man called Moustaches. He was a wonderful and fearful man. He had a son who was equally big and amazing. When both of them went to sleep, other people had to hit them with hammers in order to get them to wake up.

Now Moustaches lived in a house which was 6 miles long—as far as from here to Kitui township. He and his son had each over 200 servants. But his son had more servants than he. Both of them lived in one town, on top of the highest mountain in the country. They had bad tempers. There were many wild pigs on that mountain, so the people called it Makomanguue. Besides those hogs, there were also innumerable lions, leopards, hyenas, and zebras.

One day, Moustaches's son was seized by a lion, and he cried out loudly until his father heard it and went to help him. He found that his growing son was being bitten by a male lion, so he grabbed his son by the hand, and blew off the lion with the breath from his mouth. The lion dropped down many miles away, and by then it was completely dead. Moustaches took his son home, cared for him, and he did not die. He was a highly favoured son at that time, and he continued to grow in body and increase in strength.

When his son realized that he had now become very strong he said he would go and challenge his father to a fight, to make him know that he was a strong man. So he went to look for his father, and on the way, he met his grandmother. He hit her with one blow and she fell dead, and he continued on his way. That young man did not have a good mind, for no one would dare kill his own grandmother, unless he had a spell. When he had killed her, he went on till he came to his father's home. He began to incite his father, but his father did not get angry. After one month, Moustaches realized that his son wanted them to fight. So, one evening, after sunset, he said to him, 'Son, what exactly do you want? Do you want us to fight, or what is the matter?'

His son answered, 'Even if it were a fight, there is nothing that you can do to me. You are left completely without strength. Even if you asked someone else to help you, both of you will be unable to beat me.'

When his father heard this, he said within himself, 'I wonder what the matter is with my son? He might not be in his right mind. Why does he act like this? Or is it because I have never bothered him in any way? I will go and find out.' Now, his son had already become the king of that country.

That same evening, Moustaches went to his son and asked him, 'Do you really want to fight.' He replied, 'Father, I am completely fed up with you. I now want to hit you so you can realize that I am very angry. Try to touch me and you will see!' Moustaches said, 'Tomorrow early in the morning, when the crow has crowed, let us remove to a distant place so we can fight as much as possible. I want to beat you as thoroughly as I can. Do not go away tonight; but tomorrow morning, when I have been awakened, come to my bedroom so that we can go away together. Do not try to go back to where you have been working. You are more arrogant than you should, and tomorrow I will put away all your arrogance.' They parted and went to sleep.

Early the next morning, the servants divided themselves up: one group went to awaken the father, and the other group the son. They beat them with a hammer, as usual, until they woke up. When they got up, each cut a trunk of the wild fig-tree, the largest tree in the area, and brushed his teeth with it. When they had brushed their teeth, washed their faces, and eaten breakfast, they went out together.

When they were now many miles from their home, they started fighting. Moustaches became very angry, and so he blew off his son with his breath, and his son was thrown into the clouds above. He disappeared beyond the clouds, and after a long while, he fell down. He came running to his father and said, 'I am going to kill you this day. You had better start running away before I hit you.' Moustaches tried to escape, and his son chased him. When he got to him, he hit his father on the back again and again, until his father turned and looked, thinking that it might have been flies touching his back. But he saw that it was his son, and he continued running. He came to a high mountain and picked it up. When his son saw it, he also went and picked up his own mountain. He hit his father very hard with this mountain, and then he realized that he had better leave his own father alone, because it was through him that he had been born. But his father felt that he should not let his son continue living since he had become so disobedient and arrogant, and he continued to beat him with the mountain he had picked up. The fight went on.

At eleven o'clock, they rested for two hours, and resumed their battle in the afternoon. They fought on until sunset. They now said that they should go home. When they were on their way home, the son said to himself, 'I will now hit him unawares until he dies for ever and ever.' So he hit his father very hard, and he fell down, and followed him there and hit him again and again until he died. And that son was a very evil child, because he must have had a spell of witchcraft. When he had killed his father, he went home alone, and told the people a lie, saying 'My father was eaten by the leopards that roam about in this country. So I thought I would come home, after I failed to find him, and look after his wealth and his farms. I will now live here with you.'

And the young man lived for a few months, and then began to look for a wife. He looked and looked for many days, but the women of that land were afraid of him. They said, 'Since he killed his father, he might very likely kill us also.' So, one by one, they all went away and hid themselves in the forest.

But one day, when he was going to see his grandfather, he saw a woman on the road, and he said, 'I must hurry so I can get to talk to her.' And the woman stopped and said to herself, 'Now I will come to an agreement with this man so that he can marry me because I have no one to look after me.' So they agreed to marry each other, and when they were married, they lived happily together. After a long while, the man said he would go to look for work.

When he came home on leave, he found that his wife had a baby girl. She was a very beautiful child, glittering like the sun. The baby looked exactly like its mother, who was an exceedingly beautiful girl. The mother was very beautiful: just like the sun when it dazzles through the clouds, and as white as snow on top of a high mountain. Then he went back to the town to work, and he used to send her some money. Afterwards she gave birth to a baby boy, and her husband now returned to live at home. She became pregnant again, but there broke out an epidemic and she died while giving birth. That youngest baby died, and the father also died. Only the first two children were left, and they lived without parents.

The girl was very intelligent. She looked after her young brother until he grew to be a boy. She cultivated the garden which their father had left for them; and when her brother grew up he looked after his father's cattle. But the weeds in the the garden increased so much that the girl found it impossible to keep them from covering the entire garden. So she worked harder, both in the day time and in the early hours of the evening. When she started working in the evenings, she noticed that every time she went back to the garden in the morning, she found that some unknown people had come in the night and cultivated a large piece. This went on for two years.

One day the girl said in her heart, 'Now, when we have finished cultivating in the evening, I will come back to the garden in the middle of the night to see who actually cultivates it while we are asleep.' So she went back at midnight, and the people who weeded the garden while she was away at night, said to her, 'Why have you come here?' She answered, 'I don't know what you are asking. But I will go back to see about the welfare of my young brother.' They said, 'No matter what made you come here at this time of the night, we will go with you to your home.' She told them, 'I will go to see my brother, and then I will come back.'

Now the girl's name was Wausi, and her brother's name was Waiu. She went back to the house, and told her brother, 'I will now go to the garden to talk with the people who cultivate for us, even though I do not know them.' Then she went back, but before she got to the door, he called to her and said, 'If you leave me alone I will kill myself with the knife.' Wausi said to him, 'Oh please don't. I will not go then. You better go to sleep now.' And when he had fallen asleep, she went out quietly. When she came to the garden, she found that the two people, a man and a woman, had already gone away. So she returned to the house, and told her brother that they had already gone, and said, 'Do not tell anyone that I was informed that my garden will continue to be weeded.' But a few days later her brother died, and she was left alone. She became very unhappy.

When she went to work in the garden one morning, she found a big tree-trunk growing in the centre of the garden. The trunk said to her, 'Come and sit on me!' She said, 'No, I will not. I don't want to sit on you.' But it said, 'If you come and sit on me, I will take you to see your brother Waiu.' Then she went and sat on it.

The tree said, 'You must learn this song first, and when you have learned it, close your eyes and begin to sing it:

> "Leap, leap, O tree-trunk,
> That we may go to see Waiu." '

Wausi learned that song without difficulty, and she closed her eyes and began to sing it. The tree leaped and leaped, until they came to a wonderful and beautiful country. It was a vast and new country. There she saw her mother, and father, and Waiu, as well as her youngest brother who died at birth. This youngest brother was called Kamwila. The country was beautiful and full of peace and tranquillity.

But one day, Wausi wanted very much to return to this land where they used to live a long time ago. She became very restless, and one day her mother came to know that Wausi wanted very much to come back to this earth. She also saw that she was very friendly with her youngest brother Kamwila. So the mother, Wausi, and Kamwila had a council together, and the mother warned Wausi that if she ever desired to return to this earth again, she and Kamwila would completely destroy her.

Now Wausi did not know what she could do. Every time when her father and mother were away, she would sit on her brother Waiu, and sing that same song that the tree-trunk had taught her. She tried that many times, but he could not leap like that tree. One day her mother came to realize that Wausi still wanted to go back to the earth. So the mother went and called some people who came and dug a deep hole in the ground and covered it with a piece of leather.

Then the mother called to Wausi and said, 'Come, and take these tweezers and pluck out my eyelashes.' So Wausi went, and when she was plucking them out, she fell into the hole, and her mother quickly covered it up with earth so that it was impossible to see her. Wausi began to eat that soil, and her brother Kamwila used to go and tap on the mound. Every time he tapped, Wausi sang this song,

> 'Come and pluck out my eyelash Kamwila,
> O my dear dear Kamwila,
> Come and pluck out my eyelash Kamwila.'

So she sang that song every day, but her father did not know where she was. He asked, 'Where has Wausi gone?' but every time her mother said, 'Don't worry. She only went to fetch some water from the river.' But her father became greatly troubled when he did not see her for several days.

One day Kamwila went to his brother Waiu and said to him, 'Do you know where Wausi went?' He answered, 'No, I don't.' They stayed until that day was over. Then the following day Kamwila said to him, 'Come', and they went together, to the mound under which Wausi was buried. They tapped it and heard her voice singing. When Wausi heard it, she started to cry, and she refused to eat for many days.

15

The Story of a Poor Woman

See introductory note to Text 13.

IT is about a woman who was very poor. She thought about her poverty and then decided to go and tell the king about it. Then she went, and found the king drinking beer, and greeted him, 'Good morning, king.' 'Good morning', he returned the greeting.

'I want to speak with you, can you spare the time?'

'Yes, by all means come and speak to me.' She drew near, and said, 'I am very poor, but I have a very beautiful daughter. I will give her to you if you will help me.'

The king said, 'Go and bring her that I might see her.' The poor woman went back and came with her daughter to the king's palace. She was a very beautiful girl, and when he saw her, he fell in love with her at once, and he decided to take her to be his wife. He gave the mother of the girl a lot of money. As she went away she said to the king, 'If my daughter does not bear seven children, kill her; but if she does, you will then have to give me some cattle.' The king said, 'Very well then. I am very pleased with the agreement.'

The girl now became pregnant, and after a long time she began to travail. The king had another wife, and this first wife did not want the king to get married again. At this time the king was away on a long journey. The girl was now at the very point of giving birth, and the first wife collected seven stones and hid them in the house. When the girl produced one baby, this other wife tossed it into the river near by. The girl produced another baby, and the woman tossed it into the river. She produced the third, and the fourth, and the fifth, and the sixth, until all seven children were born, but the other woman threw them all into the river. The first wife put all the seven stones into the baby bed. When the girl had finished giving birth, she asked the other woman who had been the midwife, 'What kind of babies have I brought forth? Are they boys or girls?' The woman answered, 'You gave birth only to these seven stones!' The girl was exceedingly shocked, and she said, 'Now when my husband comes, he will surely kill me.'

Near the palace there was another woman who lived there. When she was cutting the firewood, she saw those babies floating on the water, and she took them and nursed them in her house. They were six baby boys and one baby girl. They grew up and became big children. But when the first queen, who had thrown them into the river, came to know about it, she thought of what she could do to kill one of them so that the king might never discover what had happened. She knew that if he found out, he would kill her.

So one day she went and called the boys and said to them, 'Children, who is your father?' They answered, 'We do not know.' She asked them another question, 'How many are you in your home, and who is your mother?' The boys answered, 'There are six boys and one girl.' She waited until they had gone away, and then the girl appeared, and she asked her, 'Little girl, do your brothers love you?' The girl replied, 'Yes, they do. Why do you ask me that question?' The woman said, 'When they come back, tell them to go and find you a young cobra so you can play with it, if they really love you.'

Later that day, when all the seven children were together, the girl began to cry. Her brothers asked her, 'What is the matter? Why are you crying so hard?' She said, 'I want a baby cobra so I can play with it.' Her brothers went and caught one, but none of them was bitten, which is what the queen wanted to happen so that one of the boys would die.

The little girl played with the baby cobra until evening, and then she let it go away. Her name was Katumbi. She and her six brothers sat together on one large seat, and went to sleep until the following morning. The queen came, and called the girl, and said to her, 'Little girl, do your brothers love you?' Katumbi answered, 'Yes, they do. Why do you ask me that question?' She said, 'Tell them to go and get you a young lion cub so you can play with it.'

Katumbi started to cry again, and her brothers asked her, 'What is the matter?' She told them, 'I want a lion cub to play with.' They said, 'Stop crying then, we shall go and get you one.' They really loved her. So they went into the forest and captured a lion cub, and brought it back to their sister. She played with it until evening, and then let it go back into the woods.

The next day, the same evil woman came and called her, saying, 'Little girl, do your brothers really love you?' 'Yes, they do. Why do you ask me that question?' replied the little girl. She said, 'Tell them to go and get you a young leopard so you can play with it.' So the little girl told her brothers that she wanted a leopard, and they went into the forest again and brought her a young leopard. She played with it until evening, and then let it go back into the forest.

Now the woman did not know what to do next. She thought for a long time, and decided that there was a very large and fierce animal which killed people by beheading them. The animal's name in the Kamba language was *ngaku*. This she said, was the one animal that would kill some of these six brothers. So she went to find Katumbi, and asked her the same question as before. She told the little girl, 'When your brothers come, tell them to go and get you a young *ngaku*, so that you can play with it.' Katumbi asked her brothers to get her a young *ngaku*, and they did so. When she had played with it, she let it go back into the woods.

The woman came again, and told Katumbi to ask her brothers to get her the ear of an elephant so that she could sleep on it. They went and cut one and brought it to her, and she slept on it.

Then the woman went back to Katumbi, and asked her, 'Do your six brothers love you?' She answered, 'Yes, they do. Why do you ask me that question?' 'Tell them to go and get you milk from a donkey,' she said to the little girl. When her brothers came, she cried as usual, and told them that she wanted donkey milk. They went and milked a donkey, and brought the milk to their beloved sister.

But the woman was determined to get rid of one or more of these brothers. She went to Katumbi and told her to ask her brothers to go and get her a flower from a legendary tree called *Kisulumbuku*. So she cried again, and said to them, 'I want the flower of a *Kisulumbuku*.' They told her, 'Very well. We will go and get it for you.' Their foster mother prepared lunch for them, and they went on their journey.

They travelled all morning, until about three in the afternoon. They stopped, ate their lunch, and told the youngest brother to go back home and stay with his sister while they went on looking for the tree. At night they slept in the forest, and the next morning they continued to look for the *Kisulumbuku* tree. At noon that day, they asked the next youngest brother to go back and look after the other two children. So only four of them now remained. But they did not find the tree that day, so again they slept in the wilderness.

The third day they travelled until eleven in the morning, and then asked one more brother to return to see the other children, and to assure them that they were all well. The remaining three boys continued with their search until evening. And so, day after day, they went on trying to find a *Kisulumbuku*. On the seventh day, they saw a lonely hut in the forest. It was a very ugly-looking hut.

They came to the hut, and found a very old woman. She asked them, 'Children, what are you looking for in this country where I have never seen other people before?' They answered, 'We are looking for the flower of a *Kisulumbuku* tree.'

She replied in great wonder and bewilderment, 'Ooooooo! Children, will you really be able to get it because of the owners of that tree?' They said, 'Maybe you can help us then.' She performed some magical rites on them, and gave them a charm with magical powder in it, and said to them, 'When you get there, if you find that they are absolutely quiet and still, you will know that they are not asleep. Do not go near them, but bite a little of this powder, and they will go to sleep immediately. If you find them making a lot of noise, you will know that they are completely asleep and are merely dreaming. Do not, however, under any circumstances, get into their home until and unless you have each bitten a little bit of this powder.'

The three boys went on now, and when they came to the land where the tree grew, they found the owners making a noise. They saw seven fences round their home, but the boys jumped over the fences and came to the house. They bit their charm, and were now sure all would be well. In the middle of the fenced ground they found a very tall tree, with one flower. It was the tree and the flower they had been looking for.

One of the boys climbed up the tall trees and picked the flower. They jumped the fence, and the flower shouted, 'Hoooy! Hoooy! I am now going away! It is I, the flower of a *Kisulumbuku*.' It cried out and continued to shout. The boys now ran as fast as they could. The old woman had given them three bottles, and they dropped one on the ground, and thorns grew up. But the owners of the flower woke up, and chased them, jumping over the thorns. The boys dropped down another bottle, and sisal plants grew there immediately. By the time the owners of the flower had gone over the area with sisal, the boys had already outrun them by several miles. When they realized that they were still being chased, they dropped the third bottle, and a lot of water came out of it, and covered a very vast area. The owners of the flower came to the lake, and tried to get across, but some drowned, and the others returned from chasing the boys.

When the boys finally reached their home safely, they found that the king had returned from his long journey. The eldest of them went to see him, and he said to the king, 'King, I want

you to call all people together.' He said to the boy, 'What do
you want all the people for?' The young man replied, 'You will
hear it, and see it.' So the king called up a large gathering of
people, and they all came together. The real mother of the
children was there, as well as the first wife of the king, and all
the seven children with their foster mother. They placed the
flower of the *Kisulumbuku* in the centre.

The king told the flower to speak. It said, 'Now, I was
brought from my home because of this little girl who wanted to
have me. Her mother is here, and about her I do now speak.
Many years ago there came a poor woman here, and said to the
king, "Take this my daughter to be your wife, and if she doesn't
produce seven children at one time, you will then kill her."
She became pregnant, and while you, the king, were away,
your first wife threw away all the seven children that this girl
gave birth to. They were found in the river by this other woman,
who took them, cared for them, and brought them up.

'But when your first wife saw that the children were still
living, she wanted to kill them. She asked the youngest of them,
this little girl, to ask her brothers to get for her a baby cobra, a
lion cub, a leopard cub, an ear of the elephant, and the flower
of the *Kisulumbuku* tree. I am that flower, and these are the
children. You can see the children sitting here. My duty was
therefore, to introduce them to their right mother, and to their
father the king. This therefore is the whole story, and I will now
go to my home.' Then the flower withered.

The king was greatly grieved over his first wife. He ordered
the soldiers to kill her, and they did so. He looked for the
mother of his second wife, and brought her to the palace, and
gave her a beautiful house to live in, and provided for her in
every way. The children grew up in the palace, and he rewarded the woman who had saved them and cared for them.
This is the end of the story about the flower, the queen, and the
king, as well as the poor woman.

16

Siboda

An Iraqw story collected in the field and translated by W. H. Whiteley. In order to show something of the difficulties of translation, a word-for-word translation is given first.

The Iraqw of northern Tanganyika speak a difficult and unusual language which cannot be classified into any of the known families. Numbering a little over 100,000, they live in the highlands of Mbulu district and practise a mixed agricultural-pastoral economy.

This particular example is one of the genre known as *ti'ita*. The protagonists in a *ti'ita* may be simply ordinary men and women or animals, but often the men and women are engaged in a struggle against supernatural forces. These may be personified, as in the case of the *Ama'irmi*, a female monster which lures humans to her habitation and swallows them, or quite impersonal, such as the qualities which make it possible for humans to speak with birds or animals, and thus overcome the intrigues of their kinsfolk (as in this story).

Stories such as these are told in the evening, often to children while waiting for the evening meal, but also between adults over beer, and to a critical audience the reciter often responds with a wonderful flow of language.

(i)

[Word-for-word translation.]

FATHER pits them dug for elephants catching; father this children had who two, boy elder name his was Siboda. One day they pits examining went. When they arrived thing which they saw was not there. They went back home. Next day time days few when they passed, they again returned. And it was that pits hold elephants in very same place this. Elephant said, 'Siboda help me.' He said, 'I you will not (cannot) help because father me will hit.' Brother his said, 'Don't it help leave (for) father when then he comes.' Then it said, 'I you occasion that also will help.' Siboda said, 'I father of house our if he me aims to kill, place which am I to know?' (Where shall I go?) Then it he took out, it (the pit) hoed over, when he finished brother younger him said to, 'Father (person) I will tell.' (Siboda) said, 'You do not tell!' (The other) said, 'Very well! I will not tell.' When they went back, and food was given, he (younger) said, 'Food (to) me pass over!' (Siboda) said, 'I am not full.' (The other)

'Now I'll tell, . . .' He said, 'Do not tell!' They way this continued
every day, boy elder hunger him by degrees got (smaller) he
got thin. Father him asked, he said 'Ah, son my is what, why
have you become thin, are you ill?' He said, 'A'a, no, father!'
Then mother father him she asked, 'Children when they eat
you hide.' Father way this it he did, and it was that boy younger
who elder him told, 'I now will say.' Father ears them he
placed (pricked his ears), said (Siboda) 'Thank you (here) is
porridge eat, do not tell!' Father appeared him asked, 'Thing
that what you say—I will tell now—tell me is what?' Boy
younger said, 'It is not there!' (it is nothing). (Father) he him
hit, he said, 'Let me say!' (Father said) 'Tell me!' He said,
'Occasions when pits examining we went Siboda elephant your
him released (from) in the pit middle.' He said, 'Siboda I pits
made because wealth (for) getting. If elephant had been caught
tusks its I would have drawn and them sold and then going
cows we would have got and poverty our would finish. Now you
elephant my released and (from) in the pit it took out.' He said,
'Fair enough.'

Then days few when they passed, father boy him said to,
'Come honey we will look for in the forest.' They went, when
they arrived rungs they prepared. When they were finished,
father them hit into the tree, they climbed with gourds their,
father (lit. 'old man') honey it placed in gourd; when he
finished him he said to, 'Gourd take, wait (until) I get down.
Going you get down I gourd will take.' Father when he
descended, rungs them pulled out, boy said, 'Father, why rungs
are you taking out?' He (father) said, 'I rungs taking out am
not, I place am fixing properly!' When he finished, he arrived
at bottom and then even one rung he does not leave. Boy when
he examined it was that rungs he had finished pulling out. He
said, 'Father, I how am I to descend?' (Father) told him, 'See
how elephant my you released.' He went off. It was that boy
elephants them saw in transit, he said, 'Elephants moving,
elephant of leg bad where?' 'He behind.' He waited, elephants
were passing, then elephant that one of leg bad arrived, it
looked up into tree, it said, 'Siboda is what?' Siboda him
answered, 'Time that I you was helping now today is (of) dying
my turning into.' It said, 'Spit on me, urinate on me, grass
throw on me; things these all of it they on back my fall, going

you jump on back my.' Means this it he did, he jumped, he
landed, tlikh, on back of elephant, it him went off with. Space
white (opening in the forest) when they went (came to) him it
put down, 'Place this have.' It ran off to place people cows
herding, herdsmen when they saw elephant place their running
to, they ran off, cows them it took, them it took off to place of
Siboda, him said to, 'Cows these are yours.' It again went girl
beautiful her it took among girls firewood gathering, took her
from amongst them, her it took to place of Siboda, him it said
to, 'Wife your here is!'; him it told, 'I have gone, present this,
time that me you helped in pit amongst.' Siboda cows his when
they increased and he had borne children, parents his them he
remembered, he said, 'Person whom I send is what person, to
house our, who people of house our is to bring to (place) this
because also I wealth my together if we eat is not good?' Birds
them he called, crow it he selected, he said, 'Crow milk my that
drink, I you will send.' It it (milk) drank, it he told, 'If you
arrive, what will you say?' It said, 'I will say khwaa, khwaa!' It
he drove off (because it had forgotten his instructions). He called
a kite, it told, 'I you will send, if you arrive that which you will
say is "People of house of Siboda son your me sends son is
Siboda open space them (cattle) he herds, cow he brings back,
cow that red-and-white, it is a heifer coloured red-and-white".'
Milk it he drank, it he told, 'You if you arrive, what will you
say?' Kite said, 'Tsingilili!' It he drove away, he said, 'Milk of
cattle my you it will kill.' Kite went off. Then eagle it he called,
'Eagle I you will send to house our, if you arrive what you will
say is "Mother of Siboda. . . ." Here, milk drink.' Eagle milk it
drank, it he asked, 'You if you arrive, what will you say?' It
said, 'Tsililili!' It he drove away, then wagtail it he summoned
it he told, 'Wagtail, I you will send, milk my that drink!' It
drank, it he told, 'Go people of house our, bring (them) to me,
if you arrive what you will say is, "Mother of Siboda. . . ." ' It
he asked, 'If you arrive what will you say?' It said, 'Mother of
Siboda. . . .'

Mother is skin cutting into strips, it (the wagtail) she threw at
with a knife, she said, 'Unlucky person of a mother, we, don't
for us awake memories.' Wagtail knife it carried with it went, it
carried to place of Siboda, him it told, 'I will not return, knife
this do you not see? Mother of your house it she threw (at) me.'

It he told, 'Milk drink, you go, I (you) will not be killed.' Time
second it returned, when he came song its was sung, it began
Daughter is skins sewing, at it threw again with needle. Wagtail
needle it again brought with it, came it, carried place of Siboda,
him it told, 'It do you see? daughter of house your me she threw
at with needle, skin my is bad (= is hurt), if it breaks, person
(= who?) is to pay me, children my person them will feed?'
Siboda it told, 'Children your I them will feed, you go, I (you)
will not be killed.' It again returned time third. Daughter is
dung sweeping, it she threw at with scoop. Wagtail scoop it
carried, with it went, it took place of Siboda: when it arrived
him it told, 'Do you see? daughter of house your me threw at
with scoop.' Siboda scoop that it laid aside, it he told, 'You go,
return, milk drink.' It again returned. When it arrived, old
man them cows is herding, it threw at with stick. Wagtail it
stick carried, it went (with), it carried place of Siboda. It said,
'Do you see? old man of house your me threw at with stick. I
will not return I will be killed.' Siboda it he told, 'Thank you,
drink my milk, return.' It returned, when it arrived, song it
took up, and it was that person around there is not. It moved
place of dung. Song it again took up. It was that person being
there is not. It said, 'People of house this today they have gone?'
It moved to entrance of house, singing it again took up and it
was that person saying there is not. It entered to inside, they are
hiding, it was that it moved (into) the house (room), when it
went they it seized. It said, 'Do not me kill.' 'You, thing your
(= your fate) is (for) killing, Siboda place what?' It said,
'Person one me follow.' Mother it followed, they arrived to
place of Siboda, it was that story its which true, mother son her
when she saw, she fainted, boy her he-goat killed (for). When
she recovered, him she asked, 'Son my are you alive?' He said,
'Yes, wagtail and mother people other all were brought they
brought them to place of Siboda, they lived together.'

(ii)

[*Free translation.*]

A father dug pits for catching elephants. This man had two sons,
the elder's name was Siboda. One day they went to look at the
pits. When they arrived they didn't see anything. They went
home. When a few days had passed, they returned. It so

happened that an elephant was in that very pit; the elephant
said, 'Siboda, help me?' Siboda said, 'I cannot save you else my
father will beat me.' His brother said, 'Don't help it, leave it for
father when he comes here.' Then the elephant said, 'I'll also
help you on another occasion.' Siboda said, 'If my father aims
to kill me, what place shall I know?' Then he released the
animal and dug over the pit. When he had finished, his younger
brother said, 'I'll tell father.' He said, 'You are not to tell him!'
The other said, 'Good, all right, I'll not tell him.' When they
returned home, and were given food, the younger said, 'Leave
for me your food'; the other replied, 'But I'm not full.' 'I'll tell
then', said the other. 'Don't say anything', said the elder, and
they went on like this every day, the elder son hunger getting
him, little by little, and he got thin. His father asked him, 'What
is the matter my boy?' 'Why have you become thin, are you ill?'
He said, 'No father!' The mother said to her husband, 'When
the boy eats, you hide yourself.' Their father did that. The
younger boy said to his brother, 'I'll tell.' His father pricked up
his ears. The elder said, 'Thank you, here is my porridge, but
don't tell.' Father appeared, asked him, 'That thing which you
said, "Now I'll tell", tell me what is it?' The younger said, 'It is
nothing.' Father hit him. He said, 'I'll tell you father!' 'Tell me,'
he said. 'That day we went to the pits, Siboda set free your
elephant from the trap.' Father said, 'Siboda, I built those
traps so as to get rich. The elephant if it had been caught, I
would have taken out the tusks, and sold them, and we would
have got cows (and sold them), and our poverty would have
been finished. Now you released my elephant, and set it free
from the pit.' Father said, 'Enough.' After a few days the father
said to the boy, 'Come, let us go to the forest and collect
honey.' They went, and when they arrived they prepared
rungs. When they'd finished the father began to knock them into
the tree. They climbed with their gourd. The father placed the
honey in the gourd. When he finished, he said, 'Take the gourd,
wait till I get down.' 'I'm going, then you come down and I'll
take the gourd.' The father as he descended took out the rungs;
the son said, 'Father why are you taking out the rungs?' Father
said, 'I'm not taking out the rungs, I'm fixing them properly.'
When he finished he reached the ground and did not leave a
single rung. The boy when he looked, saw that all the rungs had

finished being taken out. He said, 'Father what shall I get down with?' He said, 'Look to your own counsel for letting go my elephant.' He went off home. Then the boy saw elephants moving habitat, he said (singing), 'Elephants who move, where is the elephant with the bad leg, (is) he in the last line? . . .' He waited, the elephants were passing, then that elephant with the bad leg arrived. He looked up into that tree, 'Siboda, what's the matter?' Siboda said to him, 'That day when I helped you has now turned into my death.' Elephant said, 'Spit on me, piss on me, throw grass on me. If these things fall on my back, then you too jump on my back.' He did thus, he jumped, he fell, *tlix*, on the elephant's back, and he went off with him. When they got to a clearing, he let Siboda to the ground and said to him, 'You stay here!' The elephant ran off to a place where people were herding cattle: the herdsmen, when they saw the elephant running towards them, ran off and the elephant took the cows with him. He went off to Siboda, and said, 'These cows are yours.' He went off again, and took a beautiful girl from among those collecting firewood, and carried her to Siboda. 'Here is your wife,' the elephant said; 'I'm going, now, this is the recompense for the time when you helped me in the pit.'

Siboda, when his cows had increased and he had children, remembered his parents, and said, 'Who shall I send to our house, to bring here the folk of our house, because in my prosperity if we should eat together, is it not good?' He summoned the birds; he picked first the crow, 'You crow, drink my milk, this here, and I will send you.' It drank; he said to it, 'When you arrive, what will you say?' It said, 'I'll say, khwaa, khwaa.' He sent it away (for having forgotten what to say). He called the kite and said to it, 'I'll send you. When you arrive, you'll say (singing), "Folk of Siboda, your son has sent me, your Siboda who herds his cow in the clearing, and brings it back, the red and white cow, the cow coloured red and white".' It drank the milk, he said to it, 'When you arrive what will you say?' The kite said, 'Tsingilili!' He sent it away, 'May the milk of my cow kill you.' The kite went off. Then he called the eagle, saying, 'I'll send you to my folk. When you arrive you'll sing. . . . Drink my milk.' It drank; he asked it, 'When you arrive, what will you say?' It said, 'Tsililili!' He sent it away. Then he called a wagtail; he said to it, 'I'll send you; drink my milk.' It drank. He said to it, 'Go to my family and bring them for me; when you arrive sing. . . .' He asked it, 'When you arrive, what will you say?' It repeated the message. His mother was cutting up skin into strips and she threw a knife at it, saying, 'You unlucky person for a mother, don't awake memories in one's stomach.' The wagtail took the knife, and went with it, carried it to Siboda's place, and said to him, 'I'm not going back, do you see this knife? Your mother threw it at me.' He said to it, 'Drink some milk and go again, you'll not be killed.' The second day it returned, and when it arrived it sang its song again, it began. . . . The daughter was sewing skins, she threw the needle at it. The wagtail took it, went with it back to Siboda and said to him, 'Do you see this? A girl of your house threw this needle at me, and my skin is hurt. If it breaks who will pay me, who will feed my children?' Siboda said, 'I'll look after your children, you'll not be killed.' It returned a third time. The girl was sweeping out the dung with a scoop. She threw it at the bird. The bird took this scoop to Siboda; went back with it. When it arrived it said, 'Do you see? The girl of your house threw it at me.' Siboda put the scoop on one side, saying, 'You go back again, drink some milk.' It went back again; when it arrived the old man was herding cattle; threw a stick at it. The bird took the stick back with it and carried it back to Siboda. It said, 'Do you see, the old man of your house threw a stick at me. I'm not going back, I shall be killed.' He said to it, 'Please drink some milk, and go back again.' It went back and when it arrived, it sang its song, and there was no one around. It moved into the open space by the dung. It sang again; no one heard. It said, 'Where has everyone gone today?' It moved near to the door. It sang again; no one answered. It moved into the house; they were hiding and when it moved into the room, they seized it. It said, 'Don't kill me!' They said, 'You should be killed. Where is Siboda?' It said, 'One person should follow me.' Mother followed. They arrived at Siboda's place and it turned out that the word was true. Mother, when she saw her son, fainted. Her son killed a he-goat. When she came round, she asked him, 'My son are you still alive?' He said, 'Yes!' The wagtail and the mother went together to bring the others, they brought them to Siboda and they all lived together.

17

Chacha, Mongori's Son

Collected in the field and translated from the Kuria by
W. H. Whiteley.

The Bantu-speaking Kuria live rather more than 200 miles west-north-west of the Iraqw of the preceding story, being separated from them by the dry expanses of the Serengeti plains.

MONGORI had two sons: the elder Chacha, the younger Mwita. Mongori used to set pit-traps along the paths where animals passed, and killed those that were caught in them. One day Mongori went off to visit relatives, leaving instructions with his sons to kill and skin any animal that fell into the traps. Some time later the two boys went to look at the traps, and found an Ensaramwita[1] caught in one. They wanted to kill it, but suddenly it said, 'Children of your mother, do not kill me I beg you.' Mwita said, 'Come on, let's kill it' but Chacha demurred, 'Let us listen further to what it has to say.' The Ensaramwita continued, 'Children of your mother, save me today and I will help you in your time of trouble.' Mwita refused and was anxious to kill it, so the Ensaramwita turned to Chacha, offering again to help him in his time of trouble, if Mwita would not agree, would he, Chacha, help? Mwita grew impatient, 'Look here Chacha, if you let that Ensaramwita go, I shall tell father!' but Chacha insisted, 'I shall set the Ensaramwita free and you're not to go telling father!' Mwita struck a bargain, 'If you set it free you're to take my juniority, so that when father asks me to go errands, it is you who will go.' Chacha agreed. They set the animal free and it ran off. They returned home.

When their father came back, he asked them, 'Well, did you kill anything?' They said, 'Yes.' 'Was it an Ensaramwita?' 'No,' they confessed, 'it was another animal.'

The days went by: whenever Mwita was asked to do anything it was Chacha who went. Their father was astonished; 'What are those two boys up to?' One day Mwita was sent for

---

[1] A mythical animal; some say as large as a leopard, others as small as a civet-cat. All agree, however, on its magical powers.

and told Chacha to go, but Chacha was fed up and refused. 'I'll tell father if you don't go,' threatened Mwita. Chacha went. On another occasion Mwita was sent for and again called Chacha. Again he refused, and again Mwita threatened him. This time their father was near by and overheard the exchange, and called Mwita, asking him what he had said. Mwita came and told him that he had simply asked Chacha to go instead of himself. His father was amazed, 'What are you two playing at? Whenever I send you somewhere, you send Chacha! What does all this mean?' So saying, he hit Mwita hard, who cried out, 'Stop it you're killing me; I'll tell you! One day we were out at the traps, and found an Ensaramwita caught, but Chacha let it go and it ran off.' His father called Chacha; 'Chacha, come and listen to this!' Chacha came. 'Is it true that you set an Ensaramwita free and it escaped?' Chacha denied it, so his father hit him. 'Stop it, you're killing me!' he cried, 'yes, it is quite true.'

With this his father picked up a rope and took both it and Chacha off to the traps. When they arrived, he took the rope and bound Chacha hand and foot to a tree stump. He left him there and went off home.

During the night animals passed along the path, and, reaching the spot where Chacha was, asked, 'Is this a tree stump or a human being?' Chacha sang out, 'I'm a man not a tree stump; my father sent me hunting and I got an Ensaramwita but I let it go and it ran off.' He said this to all the animals as they passed along the path, until along came that very Ensaramwita that he had helped to escape. It, also, was wondering whether the object in front of it was a tree stump or human but Chacha again sang out, 'I'm not a tree stump I'm a man: my father sent me hunting, and I got an Ensaramwita but it escaped when I released it, so my father bound me hand and foot.'

The Ensaramwita came up, untied the rope, and carried Chacha to a rock near by, where he set him down, saying: 'Chacha, sleep here. If you hear anything during the night you're not to go and investigate until it gets light.'

Chacha went to sleep. When the sun rose he heard the sound of people and of cattle lowing, and saw that close to the rock on which he was lying was a large house. He woke up and found that the hamlet in which he was lying was a large one, and clearly wealthy. Just then he heard a voice, saying: 'Chacha, these things are all yours.'

The fame of Chacha and his wealth spread far and wide. Even his mother and father came to hear of it. His mother, indeed, came to look for him: she came to the neighbourhood for a while and then called her husband. He came asking where the son of Mongori, Chacha, was living.

People hearing this, laughed, 'Who can this fellow be, asking for Chacha, son of Mongori? If you see many children,' they said, 'they will all be Chacha's; and many womenfolk, they too, will be his. If you see cows, goats, sheep, and calves, all these will belong to him.' His father was amazed, doubting them, but others said it was certainly true. After a while he came to Chacha's homestead and saw how large it was, how many people there were, and how many cattle, sheep, and goats. Chacha came out of the house and greeted his father, gave him a stool, and begged him to be seated. Then he ordered a dog to be killed for the guest. The dog was killed, roasted, and meal was cooked. The meat was brought to his father, who ate it, and when it was finished he left and went off home.

But when he had almost reached his home he suddenly gave a bark, just like a dog, and died.

18

'Don't do what the man with the baboon with two tails did'

Collected in the field and translated from the Makonde by
W. H. Whiteley.

The Makonde live in the extreme south of Tanganyika and the northern part of Mozambique, and in contrast to the two preceding peoples are wholly agricultural.

The story given here is one of those commonly recited to children during the evening and has a strongly didactic flavour.

THERE was once a man who had a monkey (baboon) with two tails. He went to court a woman, and live with her. In this house he met two children, boys. When he had lived there for some time he told the boys, 'The day when you lose my baboon, I shall not be able to accept anything except my baboon, that is my baboon with the two tails'. One day the boys went into the bush to play, they took the baboon. When they arrived the baboon lost sight of them. The boys looked for him, but in vain, and they returned to the village. Their father told them to go and return to the bush and give him his baboon. 'If you do not get him, I shall kill you.' The children looked for iron-rations to last while they were looking for the baboon. They walked for a whole month, and one day they came across many baboons; they shouted at them saying, 'Baboon of our father, with the two tails!' The baboons replied, 'Let me look, with the one tail.' The children went off and when they had gone a little farther they came across three baboons, and one of them had two tails. They caught him and returned to the village. On the way they met an evil spirit; he asked them, 'Why are you so very thin?' They told him the whole story, and he pitied them and gave them a ball, saying, 'Tell your mother to brew beer and call folk together and play with the ball in front of them.' The boys took the ball and when they reached the village their father was pleased to get his baboon and their mother brewed beer of thanksgiving at the return of her children. On the day of the beer-drink the boys took the ball and played with it before people. If it went in at one ear it came out at the finger; if it went into the chest of one man it came out of another man's head. When their father saw that the ball was a great success he asked that it should be given to him to play with. The boys refused. Their father persisted and the boys said, 'If you lose it, we shall not want anything in its stead except our ball.' The father took the ball and threw it three times, the fourth time it stuck in his nose and wouldn't come out; he tried in vain to blow his nose to dislodge it. The boys asked, 'Now what are you going to do? We're going to cut off your nose to get the ball out.' When they cut off his nose the ball came out, but their father died. It was all the fault of the baboon.

19

The Arrival of Stanley

From *Maisha ya Hamed bin Muhammed el Murjebi yaani Tippu Tip*, trans. by W. H. Whiteley, Supplement to the *East African Swahili Committee Journals*, nos. 28/2, July 1958, and 29/1, January 1959.

Hamed bin Muhammed (1840–1905) was one of the best known of the Arab traders who, during the middle of the last century, played a great part in opening up the interior of eastern Africa to commerce and trade.

The incidents described in the following passage took place in 1876–7 when Tippu Tip was at the height of his power on the upper reaches of the Congo, and had not yet embarked upon his fatal dealings with the Belgians.

The autobiography of Tippu Tip belongs partly to oral and partly to written prose: though the style is vigorous and pungent, proper to a man of action recalling a busy and eventful life, yet it must be remembered that his audience seems not to have been a circle of kinsfolk or friends but rather a scribe. To what extent the result is due to the scribe rather than to Tippu, one cannot guess, but the narrative is certainly in keeping with what one knows of Tippu as a man, and the most notable example of its kind in Swahili. Comparison might be made with *Akiga's Story* (trans. Rupert East, O.U.P., 1939) or, for those who can read Swahili, with *Maisha ya Sameni ole Kiwasis yaani Justin Lemenye*, Nairobi, 1954.

A MONTH passed there until one afternoon Stanley appeared. We greeted him; welcomed him and gave him a house. The following morning we went to see him and he showed us a gun, telling us, 'From this gun 15 bullets come out!' Now we knew of no such gun firing 15 rounds, neither knew of one nor had seen such. I asked him, 'From a single barrel?' He said they came from a single barrel, so I asked him to fire it so that we could see. But he said we should produce a fee of 20–30 dollars for firing it once. In my heart I thought he was lying. A single-barrelled gun; the second I thought was a cleaning rod! How could the bullets come out of one barrel, one after another? I said to him, 'Over in Rumami there's a bow which takes twenty arrows. When you fire, all twenty fly together, and each arrow kills a man.' At that he went outside and fired twelve rounds. Then he took a pistol and fired six rounds. He came back and sat down on the veranda. We were amazed. I asked him how he loaded the bullets and he showed me.

Two days passed; on the third he asked me whether I knew Munza. I said, 'I neither know Munza nor have I ever heard of the country called Munza.' He told me, 'If you go to Nyangwe and go north for thirty days you'll get to Munza. Look here, you seem to me to be the right sort of person, and I'd like you to take me.' I agreed tentatively. 'Furthermore,' he said, 'I'll give you 7,000 dollars.' I told him that I wouldn't take him for the sake of 7,000 dollars and showed him the ivory I had. 'I shall go from goodwill and it won't be 7,000 dollars that seduces me from here.' Stanley was amazed at the quantity of ivory: I told him I would give him my considered answer in the morning. I slept, and on the following morning told him I would agree to take him. On the second day we set off. All my kinsmen tried to dissuade me, 'You have left your work to follow this European without knowing where he's going?' They gave up trying to dissuade me and I answered them, 'I mind my own business, not that of other people!' We set off and reached Nyangwe. There, people were more outspoken in trying to dissuade me, and derided me, 'What, going with a European, have you lost your senses?' 'You're mad, will you then become a European? Yet you're not needy, why then? You have your stock of ivory, why then follow an unbeliever?' I told them, 'Maybe I am mad, and you that are sensible, keep to your own affairs.'

We left Nyangwe, and went north through the forest where one cannot see the sun for the size of the trees, except in the clearings for cultivation or villages. We were in difficulties because of the mud, particularly those who were carrying the boats. Night came, and we slept; the boats were benighted on the road. This was a blow for the men carrying Stanley's loads and the boat. One day's journey took three days. Stanley was in despair; he said to me, 'What do you suggest? This trouble is serious; what do you say? How many days to the Congo?' I said to him, 'We've never been, but it is not far; in six or seven days we should arrive. It is the forest that is the difficulty, but the river is near.' He urged us to press on to the river.

When we got to the river we saw some locals coming with

their tiny dug-outs, two men to each vessel. They came quite close to us and we called them, but they shouted abuses at us. Stanley was particularly pleased to arrive at the river and set about assembling the boat. The locals came up close, and we called them, but again they shouted abuses at us and asked us what we were doing. We replied that we were making *wato*, that is to say dug-outs. We went on until the boat was finished. Stanley and I boarded the boat together with Abdallah bin Abed, my servant; two of my slaves, and fourteen of Stanley's men, making a total in all of eighteen men. The small dug-outs of the locals numbered more than 300. We fired several rounds and they were filled with alarm. They were called WaGenia and spent their lives fishing. Some gave themselves up, and left their canoes, of which we seized more than thirty and with which we crossed the river.

Their villages they build near the river; we saw just the empty villages, the villagers had fled. For the most part their food was bananas, and their goats were very numerous. We seized several of these. We stayed on the far bank and dispatched the boat to ferry over our men to the bank on which we were— where the villages were also. We bound two of the dug-outs together because they were so small; we had been afraid to board them and send men across, but when they were bound together, they were more sturdy, they could take four men with loads without any difficulty.

We were anxious that our men should follow the upper path, while we were in the boat and others were in the dug-outs. I harried the locals, and captured several dug-outs and goats. One day I took six or seven dug-outs and countless goats, but the locals were adept at making off in them and they have their war-drums which are called *mingungu*. These they beat in the first village, and then in the second, and every village that hears also beats the drum. You can go for two months without seeing anything but goats since they're numerous and cannot escape; the people themselves with their small dug-outs one doesn't come across, except when a bullet passes near them or actually hits them, when they throw themselves into the water and leave their vessels.

We went on until we reached the river Kasuku at the point of its confluence with the Congo from the south (i.e. from the side

of its source). By this time we had obtained sufficient boats for
Stanley and his loads. We stayed on the Kasuku for twelve
days, when Stanley said to me, 'Now you return, you have
already done me a great service, these last four months or so;
let us, however, make one effort to get two large dug-outs,
sufficient to take my donkey.' This was where Stanley and I
parted; we stayed up all night on the island to lie in wait for
the locals until we got two dug-outs large enough.

Stanley called his men together and told them, 'Now Hamed
bin Muhammed will return; and you, get busy, for we shall set
off the day after tomorrow.' His men replied, 'If Hamed bin
Muhammed returns we return too; we're not going to a foreign
place. Anyway we signed on at the coast for two years and it is
already two and a half years. If Hamed returns we insist on
returning too.' They were firm in their resolve, the men, not to
proceed farther. Stanley was very depressed, was even put off
his food, when he went to eat.

During the evening he came to see me and said, 'My scheme
has foundered if they return, and I shall have to return too. All
my trouble will have been for nothing. Will you help me?' I
replied, 'By the Grace of God I will help you.' I slept, and in the
morning went to him; I asked him, 'Well, what have you
decided?' He said, 'I have no plans nor do I know what to do.'
Then I told him, 'All right, take my advice and summon all
your men together and speak to me fiercely, say—Look here if
you return, all my men will insist on returning. Well, my business is the business of the Government, and we are in agreement
with Seyyid Barghash. If my men return, then when I return I
shall tell Seyyid Barghash that it was Hamed bin Muhammed
who ruined my trip; then your property will be seized—when
you've said that, well, leave things to me.' I left and about
noon he called me, collected his men, spoke to me as I had
instructed him—before the men—in a harsh tone. I said to
them, 'Do you hear what Stanley has to say; now set off on the
trip and go your way. He who follows me I will kill, because
you'll ruin me; my goods will become the property of the
Government; on this occasion you have killed me and all my
trouble of the past few years is lost. There is no need to die
here, is there? but if you follow me I will certainly kill you.' I
left and they also.

But during the night some of Stanley's headmen came and said to me. 'As for us and the European, our time together is finished; we are determined to go back.' I said to them, 'This won't do, get on with the trip!' They said, 'Do you want us to get lost?' I told them that his fate was their fate also; if they got lost they would get lost together. They persisted, 'This European is mean; he counts everything out; he doesn't even give us clothes, not one *shuka*[1] does he offer.' I told them to leave this to me, that I would give them what they wanted, only they must get on with the journey. They said, 'What shall we do? You, we fear and respect for your words, but we've no contract with this European. Our time is already six months overdue.' I told them that their words weren't good enough and that they should follow me. I went to Stanley and told him, 'Give me six loads of goods!' He gave me nine. I called the men and told them to take the clothes. To the senior I gave six pieces and to the juniors four. To the senior headmen I gave nine pieces to each man, which meant that a little was left over; this I returned to Stanley. They agreed readily to set off. I told Stanley to get moving. He was overjoyed, and in his lying manner, told me, 'I don't know how to pay you back, to recompense you for your kindness, nor how much to give you. But when I get back to Europe I shall receive esteem and much wealth. I'll bring you back a watch worth 1,000 dollars, mounted with diamonds, and as for money I'll bring you a countless sum; but don't leave here, wait for me a month, until I've passed safely. If I don't find the road I'll come back and we'll go to Rumami.'

I agreed, and waited a month, hearing nothing. I then left for Rumami as I had about five *frasila* (1 *frasila* = 35 lb.) of copper which I had bought for a *frasila* of beads in Kasongo. Stanley had wanted half a *frasila* and I had given it, leaving four and a half. I went to Rumami. The river Rumami rises beyond Manyema and ultimately joins the Congo. When I reached Rumami, my four *frasila* of copper yielded 200 *frasila* of ivory. I made armlets (bangles), three pounds of copper to five bangles, and two bangles for a tusk. In a month our trading was finished. Finally, I came upon two small hoes for cultivating with, in amongst the place where the tents were pitched; they were small and old; I took them from their handles and

---

[1] Piece of cloth, worn as a loin-cloth.

inserted others, and sold the two for two tusks, one each; and each tusk weighed two and a quarter *frasila*. At this time the locals did not use ivory as exchange. They hunted elephant and ate the meat but used the tusks in their homes for a stockade. With others they made pestles and mortars for their cooking bananas; these they made into a stew and ate. Others they made into flutes (?), and some they threw into the bush where they were eaten by animals, such as rats. Others rotted, giving off a stench as they decomposed.

When I'd finished we returned. From the time when we left Rumami until we reached the Congo we were engaged in fighting every day, and the road was bad. Then when we got to the Congo there was peace. The WaGenia fled to the islands. Sleeping above (on the bank), without room, we were continually fighting. Their arrows were small but poisoned. Even a scratch is fatal. These attacks did not cease until we were near Nyangwe, about four days out, that was when the fighting stopped. We appeared at Nyangwe unannounced; they had no news of our arrival until about noon when we fired several rounds. They were overjoyed at my arrival, and asked for news. I gave it to them from the beginning to the end. I slept, and the next morning went on my way to Kasongo, boarding a dug-out for a whole day and a night, arriving at our harbour by the following morning. From the river to our town Kasongo, which we had built back from the river, was a journey of two and a half hours. I reached the town and there was great rejoicing at my arrival.

I found a crowd of local agents gathered together; some coming from Ibare, from Kasongo Rushie, and others coming from Marera; there was a further crowd at my friends'; they had brought a great deal of ivory. Coming in to hear my news, they went off again straightaway to give the news that Hamed had returned.

20

How Kimyera became King of Uganda

From *My Dark Companions and Their Strange Stories*, Henry M.
Stanley, Sampson Low, Marston & Company, London, 1893

The Ganda are the most numerous, most powerful, and most
sophisticated people of Uganda, and from the earliest days of their
contact with the British there have been periodic trials of strength.

Their oral literature has been discussed at some length in H. M.
and N. K. Chadwick (op. cit.) and also R. A. Snoxall (op. cit.).
For a stimulating interpretation of the 'Kimera' legend see 'Kimera',
C. C. Wrigley, *Uganda Journal*, no. 23, 1959.

KADU was a native lad of Uganda who, having made blood-brotherhood with a young Zanzibari of his own age, asked permission to
join our expedition of 1874–7. He survived the perils of the descent of
the Congo, and in 1879 enlisted again, and served faithfully another
term of three years in Africa. He afterwards joined Mr. H. H.
Johnston on his visit to Kilimanjaro, and proved himself as devoted
to him as he had been for seven years to me. It was while road-
making along the banks of the Congo, after becoming thoroughly
conversant with the Zanzibari vernacular, that he entertained us
with his remarkable legends. Next to his countryman Sabadu, he was
the most entertaining.

One of the first tales he related to us was about Kimyera, a king of
Uganda, who by his exploits in hunting deserves to be called the
Nimrod of that country. It ran as follows:

Many ages ago Uni reigned as king over Unyoro, a great
country which lies to the north and west of Uganda. One day he
took to wife Wanyana, a woman of the neighbouring kingdom,
who on the first night she had been taken into the inner harem
manifested a violent aversion for his person. At that time a man
named Kalimera, who was a dealer in cattle, was visiting the
court, and had already resided some months there as an honoured guest of the king, on account of his agreeable manners,
and his accomplishments on the flute. During his stay he had
not failed to note the beauty of the young women who were permitted to crowd around him while he played; but it had long been
observed that he had been specially attracted by the charms of
Wanyana. It was whispered by a few of the more maliciously

disposed among the women that a meeting had taken place, and that an opportunity had been found by them to inform each other of their mutual passion. However that may be, King Uni, surprised at the dislike which she manifested towards him, forbore pressing her for the time, trustfully believing that her sentiments would change for the better after a more intimate acquaintance with him. Meantime he built for her a separate apartment, and palisaded its court closely around with thick cane. His visits were paid to her on alternate days, and each time he brought some gift of bead or bark cloth, or soft, furry hide, in the hope of winning her favour.

In time she discovered that she was pregnant, and, fearing King Uni's wrath, she made a compact with him that if he would abstain from visiting her for one month she would repay his kindness with all affection. Uni gladly consented to this proposal, and confined his attentions to sending his pages with daily greetings and gifts. Meantime she endeavoured through her own servants to communicate with Kalimera, her lover, but, though no effort on her part was wanting, she could gain no news of him, except a report that soon after she had entered the harem of Uni, Kalimera had disappeared.

In a few days she was delivered of a fine male child, but as she would undoubtedly be slain by the king if the child was discovered, she departed by night with it, and laid it, clad in fur adorned with fine bead-work, at the bottom of a potter's pit. She then hastened to a diviner in the neighbourhood, and bribed him to contrive in some way to receive and rear her child until he could be claimed. Satisfied with his assurance that the child would be safe, Wanyana returned to her residence at the court in the same secret manner that she had left it.

Next morning Mugema, the potter, was seen passing the diviner's door, and was hailed by the great witch-finder.

'Mugema,' said he, 'your[1] pots are now made of rotten clay. They are not at all what they used to be. They now crumble in the hand. Tell me why is this?'

'Ah, doctor, it is just that. I thought to bribe you to tell me, only I did not wish to disturb you.'

'It is well, Mugema; I will tell you why. You have an enemy

---

[1] One or two small amendments to the text as originally published have been made in order to bring it more into line with current English usage.

who wishes evil to you, but I will defeat his projects. Hurry to your pit, and whatever living thing you find there, keep and rear it kindly. While it lives you are safe from all harm.'

Wondering at this news Mugema departed from the diviner's house, and proceeded to the pit where he obtained his clay. Peering softly over the edge of the pit, he saw a bundle of bark cloth and fur. From its external appearance he could not guess what this bundle might contain, but, fearing to disturb it by any precipitate movement, he silently retreated from the pit, and sped away to tell his wife, as he was in duty bound, and obtain her advice and assistance, for the wife in all such matters is safer than the man. His wife on hearing this news cried out at him, saying:

'Why, what a fool you are! Why did you not do as the diviner commanded you? Come, I will go with you at once, for my mind is troubled with a dream which I had last night, and this thing you tell me may have a weighty meaning for us both.'

Mugema and his wife hurried together towards the clay-pit, and as her husband insisted on it, she crept silently to its edge to look down. At that moment the child uttered a cry and moved the clothes which covered it.

'Why, it is a babe,' cried the woman; 'just as I found it in my dream. Hurry, Mugema. Descend quickly, and bring it up to me; and take care not to hurt it.'

Mugema wondered so much at his wife's words that he almost lost his wits, but being pushed into the pit he mechanically obeyed, and brought up the bundle and its living occupant, which he handed to his wife without uttering a word.

On opening the bundle there was discovered the form of a beautiful and remarkably lusty child, of such weight, size, and form, that the woman exclaimed:

'Oh! Mugema, was ever anybody's luck like this of ours? My very heart sighed for a child that I could bring up to be our joy, and here the good spirits have given to us the pick of all the world. Mugema, your fortune is made.'

'But whose child is it?' asked Mugema, suspiciously.

'How can I tell you that? Had you not brought the news to me of it being in the pit, I should have been childless all my life. The diviner who directed you hither is a wise man. He knows the secret, I warrant him. But come, Mugema, drop these silly thoughts. What do you say? Shall we rear the child, or leave it here to perish?'

'All right, wife. If it prove of joy to you, I shall live content.'

Thus it was that the child of Wanyana found foster-parents, and no woman in Unyoro could be prouder of her child than Mugema's wife came to be of the foundling. The milk of woman, goat, and cow was given to him, and he throve prodigiously; and when Mugema asked the diviner what name would be fittest for him, the wise man said:

'Call him Kimyera—"the mighty one".'

Some months after this, when Kimyera was about a year old, Wanyana came to the potter's house to purchase pots for her household, and while she was seated in the porch selecting the soundest among them, she heard a child crying within.

'Ah, has your wife had a child lately? I did not observe or hear when I last visited you that she was likely to become a mother.'

'No, princess,' replied Mugema; 'that is the cry of a child I discovered in the clay-pit about a year ago.'

Wanyana's heart gave a great jump, and for a moment she lost all recollection of where she was. Recovering herself with a great effort, she bade Mugema tell her all about the incident: but while he related the story, she was busy thinking how she might assure herself of his secrecy if she declared herself to be the mother of the child.

Mugema, before concluding his story, did not fail to tell Wanyana how for a time he had suspected his wife of having played him falsely, and that though he had no grounds for the suspicion further than that the clay-pit was his own and the child had been found in it, he was not quite clear in his mind yet, and he would be willing to slave a long time for any person who could thoroughly disabuse his mind of the doubt, as, with that exception, his wife was the cleverest and best woman in Unyoro.

Wanyana, perceiving her opportunity, said:

'Well, much as I affected not to know about the child, I know whose child it is, and who placed it in the pit.'

'You, princess!' he cried.

'Yes, and, if you will take an oath upon the great Muzimu to keep it secret, I will disclose the name of the mother.'

'You have my assurance of secrecy upon condition that the

child is not proved to be my wife's. Whosoever else's it may be, matters not to me; the child was found, and is mine by right of the finder. Now name the mother, princess.'

'Wanyana!'

'Yours?'

'Even so. It is the offspring of fond love, and Kalimera of Uganda is his father. The young man belongs to one of the four royal clans of Uganda, called the Elephant clan. He is the youngest son of the late king of Uganda. To him, on his father's death, fell his mother's portion, a pastoral district rich in cattle not far from the frontier of Unyoro. It was while he drove fat herds here for sale to Uni that he saw and loved me, and I knew him as my lover. Dreading the king's anger, he fled, and I was left loveless in the power of Uni. One night the child was born, and in the darkness I crept out of the king's court, and bore the babe to your pit. To the wise man I confided the secret of that birth. You know the rest.'

'Princess, my wife never appeared fairer to me than she does now, and I owe the clear eye to you. Rest in peace. My wife loves the babe, let her nurse it until happier times, and I will guard it safe as though it were mine own. Yes, the babe, I feel assured, will pay me well when he is grown. The words of the wise man come home to me now, and I see whereby good luck shall come to all. If bone and muscle can make a king, Kimyera's future is sure. But come in to see my wife, and to her discretion and wisdom confide your tale frankly.'

Wanyana soon was hanging over her child, and, amid tears of joy, she made Mugema's wife acquainted with his birth, and obtained from her earnest assurance that he would be tenderly cared for, and her best help in any service she could perform for Kimyera and his mother.

Great friendship sprang up between Princess Wanyana and the potter Mugema and his wife, and she found frequent excuses for visiting the fast-growing child.

Through the influence of the princess, the potter increased in riches, and his herds multiplied; and when Kimyera was grown tall and strong, he was entrusted by his foster-father with the care of the cattle, and he gave him a number of strong youths as assistants. With these Kimyera indulged in manly games, until he became wonderfully dexterous in casting the spear, and drawing the bow, and in wrestling. His swiftness exceeded that of the fleetest antelope; no animal of the plain could escape him when he gave chase. His courage, proved in the defence of his charge, became a proverb among all who knew him. If the cry of the herdsman warned him that a beast sought to prey upon the cattle, Kimyera never lost time to put himself in front, and, with spear and arrow, he often became victor.

With the pride of becoming the possessor of so many admirable qualities, he would drive his herds right through the cornfields of the villagers, and to all remonstrances he simply replied that the herds belonged to Wanyana, favourite wife of Uni. The people belonged to her also, as well as their corn, and who could object to Wanyana's cattle eating Wanyana's corn?

As his reputation for strength and courage was well known, the villagers then submissively permitted him to do as he liked.

As he grew up in might and valour, Uni's regards cooled towards Wanyana, and, as she was not permitted that freedom formerly enjoyed by her, her visits to Kimyera ceased. Mugema sympathized with the mother, and contrived to send Kimyera with pots to sell to the people of the court, with strict charge to discover every piece of news relating to the Princess Wanyana. The mother's heart dilated with pride every time she saw her son, and she contrived in various ways to lengthen the interview. And each time he returned to his home he carried away some gift from Wanyana, such as leopard-skins, strings of beast-claws, beads and crocodile-teeth, girdles of white monkey-skin, parcels of ground ochre, or camwood, or rare shells, to show Mugema and his wife. And often he used to say, 'Wanyana bade me ask you to accept this gift from her as a token of her esteem,' showing them similar articles.

His mother's presents to him in a short time enabled him to purchase two fine large dogs—one was black as charcoal, which was named by him Msigissa, or 'Darkness', the other was white as a cotton tuft, and called Sema-gimbi, or 'Wood-burr'. You must know that it is because of the dog Darkness, that the Baboon clan of Uganda became so attached to black dogs, and perpetuate the memory of Kimyera.

When he had become the owner of Darkness and Wood-burr, he began to absent himself from home for longer periods, leaving the herds in charge of the herdsmen. With these he

explored the plains, and hills, and woods to a great distance
from his home. Sometimes he would be absent for weeks, causing great anxiety to his kind foster-parents. The farther he went
the more grew his passion to know what lay beyond the furthest
ridge he saw, which, when discovered, he would be again
tempted to explore another that loomed in the far distance
before him. With every man he met he entered into conversation, and obtained a various knowledge of things of interest
relating to the country, the people, and the chiefs. In this manner before many months he had a wide knowledge of every road
and river, village and tribe, in the neighbouring lands.

On his return from these daring excursions, he would be
strictly questioned by Mugema and his wife as to what he had
been doing, but he evaded giving the entire truth by rehearsing
the hunting incidents that attended his wanderings, so that they
knew neither the lands he had seen, nor the distances that he
had travelled. However, being uneasy in their minds they communicated to Wanyana all that was related to them and all
they suspected. Wanyana then sought permission to pay a visit
to the potter and his wife, and during the visit she asked
Kimyera, 'Pray, tell me, my son, whither do you travel on these
long journeys of yours to seek for game?'

'Oh! I travel far through woods, and over grassy hills and
plains.'

'But is it in the direction of sunrise, or sunset, is it north or is
it south of here?'

To which he replied: 'I seek game generally in the direction
whence the sun rises.'

'Ah!' said Wanyana, 'in that way lies Ganda, where your
father lives, and whence he came in former days to exchange
cattle for salt and hoes.'

'My father! What may be my father's name, mother?'

'Kalimera.'

'And where did he live?'

'His village is called Willimera, and is near the town of Bakka.'

'Bakka! I know the town, for in some of my journeys I
entered a long way into Uganda, and have chased the leopard
in the woods that border the stream called Myanja, and over
the plains beyond the river many an antelope has fallen a
victim to my spear.'

'It is scarcely credible, my son.'

'No, but it is true, mother.'

'Then you must have been near Willimera in that case, and
it is a pity that you were not seen by your father, and been
received by him.'

A few days later Kimyera slung his knitted haversack over his
shoulder, and with shield, two spears, and his faithful dogs
Darkness and Wood-burr, he strode out of the potter's house,
and set his face once more towards the Myanja river. At the
first village across the stream he questioned the people if they
knew Willimera, and was told that it was but eight hours east.
The next day he arrived, and travelled round the village, and
rested that night at the house of one of the herdsmen of Kalimera. He made himself very agreeable to his host, and from him
he received the fullest information of all matters relating to his
father.

The next day he began his return to Unyoro, which he
reached in two weeks. He told Mugema and his foster-mother of
his success, and they sent a messenger to apprise Wanyana that
Kimyera had returned home.

Wanyana, impatient to learn the news, arrived that night at
Mugema's house, and implored Kimyera to tell her all that he
had heard and seen.

'In brief, it is this,' replied Kimyera. 'I now know certainly
where Kalimera lives. I have gone round the village, I know
how many people are in it, how many herds of cattle, and how
many herdsmen and slaves he has. Kalimera is well. All these I
learned from one of his chief herdsman with whom I rested a
night. I came here straight to let you and my foster-parents
know it.'

'It is very well, my son. Now Mugema, it is time to move,'
she said to the potter. 'Uni daily becomes more intolerable to
me. I never have yet slept with him as his wife, and I have been
true to the one man who seemed to me to be the comeliest of his
kind. Now that I know Kalimera lives, my heart has gone to
him, though my body is here. Mugema, speak, my friend.'

'Wanyana, my wit is slow and my tongue is heavy. You know
my circumstances. I have one wife, but many cattle. The two
cows, Namala and Nakaombeh, which you gave me at first, I
possess still. Their milk has always been abundant and sweet,

Namala has sufficed to nourish Kimyera into perfect lustiness and strength; Nakaombeh gives more than will feed my wife and me. Let Kimyera take his flute, his dogs, Darkness and Wood-burr, his spears and shield; Sebarija, my cowherd, who taught Kimyera the flute, will also take his flute and staff, and drive Namala and Nakaombeh. My wife will carry a few furs, some of the spoils won by Kimyera's prowess; and, lo! I and my family will follow Wanyana.'

'A true friend you have been to me and mine, Mugema! We will hence before dawn. In Willimera you will receive tenfold what you leave here. The foundling of the clay-pit has grown tall and strong, and at last he has found the way to his father and his father's kindred.'

And as Wanyana advised, the journey was undertaken that night, and before the sun arose Wanyana, Mugema and his wife, the slave Sebarija driving the two cows, Namala and Nakaombeh, were far on their way eastward, Kimyera and his two dogs, Darkness and Wood-burr, preceding the emigrants and guiding the way. The food they took with them sustained them for two days; but on the third day they saw a lonely buffalo, and Kimyera, followed by Mugema and Sebarija, chased him. The buffalo was uncommonly wild, and led them a long chase, far out of sight of the two women. Then Mugema reflected that they had done wrong in thus leaving the two women alone, and called out to Sebarija to hurry back, and to look after the women and two cows. Not long after, Darkness fastened his fangs in the buffalo, until Wood-burr came up and assisted him to bring it to the ground, and there they held him until Kimyera gave him his death-stroke. The two men loaded themselves with the meat, and returned to the place where they had left, but alas! they found no traces of the two women, nor of Sebarija and the two cows.

Day after day Kimyera and Mugema hunted all around the country for news of the missing party, until, finally, to their great sorrow, they were obliged to abandon the search, and came to the conclusion that it was best for them to continue their journey and trust to chance for the knowledge they desired.

Near Ganda another buffalo was sighted by Kimyera, and, bidding Mugema remain at the first house he came to, he went after it with his dogs. The buffalo galloped far, and near noon

he stood still under the shelter of a rock. Kimyera bounded to
the top, and, exerting all his strength, he shot his spear clean
through the back of the animal. That rock is still shown to
strangers as the place where Kimyera killed the first game in
Uganda, and even the place where he stood may be seen by the
marks of his feet which were impressed on it. While resting on
the rock he saw a woman pass near by with a gourd of water.
He called out to her, and begged for a drop to allay his thirst.
She smilingly complied, as the stranger was comely and his
manner pleasant. They entered into conversation, during which
he learned that she belonged to Ganda, and served as maid to
Queen Naku, wife of Sebwana, and that Naku was kind to
strangers, and was famed for her hospitality to them.

'Do you think she will be kind to me?' asked Kimyera. 'I am
a native of Unyoro, and I am seeking a house where I may
rest.'

To which the maid replied: 'It is the custom of Naku, and,
indeed, of all the princes of Ganda, to entertain the stranger,
since, in the far olden times, the first prince settled in this land
in which he was a stranger. But what may that be which is
secured in your girdle?'

'That is a reed flute on which I imitate, when alone, the
songs of such birds as sound sweetest to me.'

'And are you clever at it?' asked the maid.

'Judge for yourself,' he said; and forthwith blew on his flute
until the maid marvelled greatly.

When he had ended, she clapped her hands gaily and said:
'You will be more than welcome to Naku and her people.
Make haste and follow me that I may show you to her, for your
fortune is made.'

'Wait: I have a companion not far from here, and I must not
lose him. But you may say you have met a stranger who, when
he has found his friend, will present himself before Queen
Naku and Sebwana before sunset.'

The maid withdrew and Kimyera rose, and cutting a large
portion of the meat he retraced his steps, and sought and found
Mugema, to whom he told all his adventures.

After washing the stains of travel and refreshing themselves,
they proceeded into the village to the residence of the queen
and her consort Sebwana. Naku was prepared by the favourable

reports of the maid to receive Kimyera kindly, but when she saw his noble proportions and handsome figure she became violently in love with him, and turning to Sebwana she said:

'See now, we have guests of worth and breeding. They must have travelled from a far land, for I have heard of no tribe which could boast such a youth as this. Let us receive him and his old friend nobly. Let a house close by our own be made ready for his lodging, and let it be furnished with abundance of food, with wine (banana wine) and milk, bananas and yams, water and fuel, and let nothing be lacking to show our esteem for them.'

Sebwana gave orders accordingly and proceeded to select a fit house as a lodging for the guests.

Then Naku said: 'I hear that you are skilled in music. If that is the instrument in your girdle with which you have delighted my maid, I should be pleased to hear you.'

'Yes, Queen Naku, it is my flute; and if my music will delight you, my best efforts are at your service.'

Then Kimyera, kneeling on the leopard skins placed for the convenience of himself and Mugema, took out his flute, and after one or two flourishes, poured forth such melodious sounds that Naku, unable to keep her eyes open, closed them and lay down with panting breasts, while her senses were filled as it were, with dreams of happier lands, and faces of brighter people than ever she knew in real life. As he varied the notes, so varied the gladsome visions of her mind. When the music gently vibrated on her ears, her body palpitated under the influence of the emotions which swayed her; when they became more enlivened she tossed her arms about, and laughed convulsively; and when the notes took a solemn tone, she sighed and wept as though all her friends had left her only their tender memory. Grieved that Naku should suffer, Kimyera woke the queen from her sorrowful condition with tones that soon started her to her feet, and lo, all at once, those who were present joined in the lively dance, and nothing but gay laughter was heard from them. Oh, it was wonderful what quick changes came over people as they heard the flute of Kimyera. When he ceased, people began to look at one another in a foolish and confused way, as though something very strange had happened to them.

But Naku quickly recovered, and went to Kimyera, smiling and saying:

'It is for you to command, Kimyera. To resist your flute would be impossible. Again welcome to Ganda, and we shall see if we cannot keep you and your flute amongst us.'

She conducted Kimyera and his foster-father Mugema to their house. She examined carefully the arrangements made by the slaves, and when she found anything amiss she corrected it with her own hands. Before she parted from them she called Mugema aside, and questioned him further respecting the youth, by which means she obtained many interesting particulars concerning him.

On arriving at her own house she called all the pages of the court to her, and gave orders that if Sebwana told them to convey such and such things to the strangers next day, that none of them should do so, but carry them to the rear court where only women were admitted.

In consequence of this command Mugema and Kimyera found themselves deserted next day, and not one person went near them. Mugema therefore sought an interview the day after with Queen Naku and said:

'The custom of this country seems strange to us, O Queen. On the first day we came your favours showered abundance on us, but on the next not a single person showed his face to us. Had we been in a wilderness we could not have been more alone. It is possible that we may have offended you unknown to ourselves. Please acquaint us with our offence, or permit us to depart at once from Ganda.'

'No, Mugema, I must ask you to be patient. Food you shall have in abundance, through my women, and much more is in store for you. But come, I will visit the young stranger, and you shall lead me to him.'

Kimyera had been deep in thought ever since he had parted from Naku, and he had not observed what Mugema had complained of; but on seeing Naku enter his house, he hurried and laid matting on the floor, and, covering it with leopard skins, begged Naku to be seated on them. He brought fresh banana-leaves in his arms, and spread them near her, on which he arranged meat and salt, and bananas and clotted milk, and kneeled before her like a ready servitor.

Naku observed all his movements, her admiration for his person and graces of body becoming stronger every minute. She peeled a ripe banana and handed it to him, saying: 'Let Kimyera taste and eat with me and then I will know that I am in the house of a friend.'

Kimyera accepted the gift with thanks, and ate the banana as though he had never eaten anything so delicious in his life. Then he also peeled a beautiful and ripe banana, and, presenting it to her on a fragment of green leaf with both hands, said to her:

'Queen Naku, it is the custom of my country for the master of the house to wait upon his guests. Wherefore accept, O Queen, this banana as a token of friendship from the hands of Kimyera.'

The queen smiled, bent forward with her eyes fixed on his own, and took the yellow fruit, and ate it as though such sweetness was not known in the bananaland of Ganda.

When she had eaten she said:

'Listen, Kimyera, and you, Mugema, listen well, for I am about to utter weighty words. In Ganda, since the death of my father, there has been no king. Sebwana is my consort by choice of the elders of the land, but in name only. He is really only my *katikiro* (Premier). But I am now old enough to choose a king for myself, and according to custom, I may do so. Wherefore I make known to you, Mugema, that I have already chosen my lord and husband, and he by due right must occupy the chair of my father, the old king who is dead. I have said to myself since the day before yesterday that my lord and husband shall be Kimyera.'

Both Kimyera and Mugema prostrated themselves three times before Naku, and, after the youth had recovered from his confusion and surprise, he replied:

'But, Queen Naku, have you thought what the people will say to this? May it not be that they will ask, "Who is this stranger that he should reign over us?" and they will be angry with me and try to kill me?'

'No. For you are my father's brother's son, as Mugema told me, and my father having left no male heirs of his body, his daughter may, if she choose, ally herself with a son of his brother. Kalimera is a younger brother of my father. You see, therefore, that you, Kimyera, have a right to the king's chair, if I, Naku, will it to be so.'

'And how, Naku, do you propose to act? In your cause my arm is ready to strike. You have but to speak.'

'In this way. I will now leave you, for I have some business for Sebwana. When he has gone I will then send for you, and you, when you come to me, must say, "Naku, I have come. What can Kimyera do for Queen Naku?" And I will rise and say, "Kimyera, come and seat yourself in your father's brother's chair." And you will step forward, bow three times before me, then six times before the king's chair, and, with your best spear in hand and shield on arm, you will proceed to the king's chair, and turning to the people who will be present, say in a loud voice thus: "Lo, people of Ganda! I am Kimyera, son of Kalimera, by Wanyana of Unyoro. I hereby declare that with her own free will I this day do take Naku, my father's brother's daughter, to wife, and seat myself in the king's chair. Let all obey, on pain of death, the king's word."'

'It is well, Naku; be it according to your wish,' replied Kimyera.

Naku departed and proceeded in search of Sebwana; and, when she found him, she affected great distress and indignation.

'How is this, Sebwana? I gave orders that our guests should be tenderly cared for and supplied with every needful thing. But I find, on inquiring this morning, that all through yesterday they were left alone to wonder at our sudden disregard for their wants. Haste, my friend, and make amends for your neglect. Go to my fields and plantations, collect all that is choicest for our guests, lest, when they leave us, they will proclaim our unkindness.'

Sebwana was amazed at this charge of neglect, and in anger hastened to find out from the pages. But the pages, through Naku's good care, absented themselves, and could not be found; so that old Sebwana was obliged to depend upon a few unarmed slaves to drive the cattle and carry the choicest treasures of the queen's fields and plantations for the use of the strangers.

Sebwana having at last left the town, Naku returned to Kimyera, whom she found with a sad and disconsolate aspect.

'Why, what ails you, Kimyera?' she asked. 'The chair is now vacant. Arm yourself and follow me to the audience court.'

'Ah, Naku! I but now remembered that as yet I know not whether my mother and good nurse are alive or dead. They may be waiting for me anxiously somewhere near the Myanja, or their bones may be bleaching on one of the great plains we traversed in coming hither.'

'Nay, Kimyera, my lord, this is not a time for mourning. Bethink thee of the present needs first. The chair of the king awaits you. Rise, and occupy it, and tomorrow all Ganda is at your service to find your lost mother and nurse. Come, delay not, lest Sebwana return and take vengeance on us all.'

'Fear not, Naku, it was but a passing fit of grief which filled my mind. Sebwana must needs be strong and brave to dispossess me when Naku is on my side,' saying which Kimyera dressed himself in war-costume, with a crown of cock's-tail feathers on his head, a great leopard skin depending from his neck down his back, a girdle of white monkey skin round his waist, his body and face brilliantly painted with vermilion and saffron. He then armed himself with two bright shining spears of great length, and bearing a shield of dried elephant hide, which no ordinary spear could penetrate, he strode after Queen Naku towards the audience court in the royal palace. Mugema, somewhat similarly armed, followed his foster-son.

As Kimyera strode proudly on, the great drum of Ganda sounded, and its deep tones were heard far and wide. Immediately the populace, who knew well that the summons of the great drum announced an important event, hastily armed themselves, and filled the great court. Naku, the queen, they found seated in a chair alongside of the king's chair, which was now unfilled, and in front of her was a tall young stranger, who prostrated himself three times before the queen. He was then seen bowing six times before the empty king's chair. Rising to his feet, he stepped towards it, and afterwards faced the multitude, who were looking on wonderingly.

The young stranger, lifting his long spears and raising his shield in an attitude of defence, cried out loud, so that all heard his voice:

'Lo, people of Ganda! I am Kimyera, son of Kalimera, by Wanyana of Unyoro. I hereby declare that with her own free will I this day do take Naku, my father's brother's daughter, to wife, and seat myself in the king's chair. Let all obey, on pain of death, the king's word.'

On concluding this address, he stepped back a pace, and gravely sat in the king's chair. A loud murmur rose from the multitude, and the shafts of spears were seen rising up, when Naku rose to her feet, and said:

'People of Ganda, open your ears. I, Naku, the legitimate queen of Ganda, hereby declare that I have found my father's brother's son, and I, this day, of my own free will and great love for him, do take him for my lord and husband. By full right Kimyera fills the king's chair. I charge you all henceforth to be loyal to him, and him only.'

As she ended her speech the people gave a great shout of welcome to the new king, and they waved their spears, and clashed them against their shields, thus signifying their willing allegiance to King Kimyera.

(21–23)

THREE LUGBARA MYTHS

The following three stories were collected in the field and translated from the Lugbara by Dr. J. Middleton

The Lugbara live in the extreme north-west of Uganda and the adjoining areas of the Congo Republic.

The first story tells how lightning visited the people of the clan Aiiku. Today if a person thinks he may be struck by lightning he will say, 'I am a man of Aiiku', and the lightning will then avoid him. Lightning is regarded as a manifestation of power of Divinity, and a person killed by lightning is considered to have been marked out in a special way by God. At a time of serious drought, a sheep is driven into the mountains, where it is said to become lightning and to bring rain.

The second story is one of the myths of the creation of the world and society. Usually Arube and O'duru are given as the first children of an original pair created by God, Gborogboro and Meme; but the order of names of mythical sibling-pairs in these myths is rarely the same. Arube is said to mean 'maker of miracles' and O'duru means 'miraculous omen'; they are thus marked off from later and ordinary ancestors as being miraculous and unhuman, while their incest means that they were ignorant of the ties of kinship and so asocial or presocial—society had not yet been formed. References to the myth are given in J. Middleton, *Lugbara Religion* (1960), ch. v, and 'Some Social Aspects of Lugbara Myth', *Africa*, xxiv (1954).

The last story is part of the most widespread myth of the Lugbara, that dealing with Dribidu and Jeki (here called Agalaha). A long and fuller version is given by J. P. Crazzolara, *The Lwoo*, vol. iii, pp. 350 ff., where Dribidu ('the hairy one') is called Tereo or Banyale ('eater of men'). Reference to it is also made in J. Middleton, *Lugbara Religion*, ch. v, and 'Some Social Aspects of Lugbara Myth'.

This myth deals with the two founding ancestors of the Lugbara, who are generally given as the sons of a line of incestuous sibling-pairs (see myth of Arube and O'duru). They led the Lugbara from an original home in the north into their present country, and so established society. They were themselves, however, personages of myth, shown by their miraculous abilities and the fact that they were cannibals. In the version given here, emphasis is placed on the wanderings of the Lugbara, whereas in most versions emphasis is placed rather on their 'inverted' characteristics and their discovery of autochthonous leper women by whom they had sixty sons who were to become the founders of the sixty Lugbara clans. In this version they are already given children before they entered Lugbara, but this is unusual.

21

I. How Lightning bore Children on Earth

LONG ago a man of this country dug a large field. The field produced a very large amount of millet. Seeing that he had so much millet he decided to make a very big granary for storing it. When harvest came the millet was collected and stored in the granary. The big granary they made was too small for all the millet. They therefore compressed it by using logs and other heavy objects. When the millet was all stored and the work completed a heavy rain fell. As it was falling lightning came down in the form of a sheep; its body and wool were all white.

The lightning opened the granary with its wings and entered it. The owner of the granary then opened it so that the lightning could get out. The lightning then prepared a very good place on top of the stored millet for laying eggs. This was said to be the mother lightning, and the father was up in the sky. The father then threw a white substance like cloth to the ground for the mother to be taken up again. The following day nothing happened. The lightning rested and the next day it descended to that village and again opened the granary with its wings, entered it and laid an egg. After that it flew up to the father. After that it again took a day's rest. The following day it laid a second egg. It repeated these actions until they amounted to three.

When there were three eggs the mother lightning descended every day to visit the eggs in the granary. It was fed on un-squeezed[1] beer. The owner of the millet therefore had to collect that kind of food from the surrounding villages. Besides that, his wife made beer every day. They were very careful to do this because when the lightning came down and found no food it destroyed very many things like pots and granaries and even set huts on fire. For that reason the people feared it very much. They kept on bringing the food for the lightning and were waiting for the time when the eggs would hatch. No one knew how long it would take. When three weeks had passed the eggs then hatched. The eggs were divided into six magnificent calabashes. When the eggs had hatched both the mother lightning and the father lightning came down every day to their children to teach them how to fly. Each day they flew a short distance until they were well trained. When the children were strong enough they flew up. The six beautiful calabashes were left at the village. Afterwards the mother and father came down to the village. By then the owner of the millet had made beer and had made a great feast for his people. The elders had gathered, questioning each other why the lightning had done these things.

Immediately after the feast the lightning divided the calabashes among the people. It gave two to the owner of the millet. Two calabashes were then given to the next-door village, one to another small village, and the other to another small village. It also gave the people a kind of medicine which was to be planted and kept for ever. It was to be used when a man was struck by lightning. Another day the lightning came down and set fire to a large area of grass. The man who was to take care of the lightning shouted and said, 'Put out all the fire you have with you at home, come and fetch this fire brought to us by the lightning.' The fire was very bright and all of the people of that place took it and for a long time people talked of it.

The lightning used to come down to his people but these days it does not.

---

[1] Unsqueezed beer is used in certain rites as offering to the dead and to God. It is not drunk in non-ritual situations before it is squeezed.

22

II. The First People to have lived here

EVER since the world was created no man had lived in this country. After a long time a man by the name Arube and a woman O'duru came to this country by the way of Kakwa.[1] As they were coming they did not know where they were going, but thought they would find human beings. As they were coming along their way they slept in caves and the only food they ate was fruit.[2] When they arrived here they went everywhere to search for human beings. As they wandered about they did not meet anyone. When they found out that there was no one who lived in this country they decided to settle in a place and to rest. Arube was O'duru's brother, but finding no one to marry he married his sister.

When the two had married they had many children. Those children took their sisters as wives. Each one had children and in that way people became numerous. Being many in one home quarrels soon arose between them.

When Arube saw that his children were quarrelling he decided to separate them. He divided them into groups and opened new homes near the main home so as to stop quarrels. The people of those new homes also did the same as did Arube, and they married their sisters. This continued until many of their children spread all over the country.

23

III. Dribidu and Agalaha

LONG ago before we came to this country Dribidu was our ancestor. Dribidu and his wife had many children. When the children became numerous the land in which they settled was overcrowded. Those children were divided into small lineages.[3] One lineage was said to be of the same mother and the other of

[1] i.e. they came from the north.
[2] Or wild, uncultivated food: there was as yet neither settlement nor cultivation.
[3] The Lugbara word is *suru*, a lineage, clan, or tribe.

the same father to another, and people argued as to who were the more senior.

Seeing that the place in which his grandchildren had settled was overcrowded he decided to find a piece of land in which to open a settlement.

One day Dribidu collected all his people together. During the meeting he explained all his troubles and told them to gather all their cattle and other things so that they could move about in search of a piece of land in which to open up a new settlement.

Those people then collected all their cattle together. Besides that, each man collected seeds. When everything was ready they started on their way with their animals. After a long period of travelling Dribidu would stop them to see whether all were present. Many told him that their brothers were missing. For that reason Dribidu then told them to rest and wait for those who were behind. He then sent his brother Agalaha to go and see where they were.

Agalaha was to take the drum with him and when he was half-way he was to beat it. Each time those people heard the drum they would say, 'Let us take courage and follow them, let us not let them leave us behind.' In that way they slowly followed.

Each time Agalaha went back he came back to Dribidu when those people were close to the first group. The first group would push ahead and again stop when the second group were left behind. Dribidu would then command them to gather together and wait for those left behind. He would again send his brother Agalaha to lead those who were lost. Every now and then he was sent with the drum. He was to beat it each time he thought he was half-way and the second group was to follow the beating of the drum. Dribidu and his brother Agalaha kept on repeating the same action. In that way their grandchildren came up to this place.

The second group was slow in coming because they were more than those who were in front of them, and their cattle and seeds were also more and so they had more to carry. After a long period of travelling Dribidu got tired of stopping. He took a long time waiting for those who were following close to him. When he had collected enough they came ahead without stopping until he reached this country. When those people arrived in this country they established settlements according to their lineages as they had been in their former country. When all had settled Dribidu decided to go back and bring those who were left. Before he went, many other people passed by who were not of his country.

One of those lineages who were passing ahead borrowed the drum from Dribidu. After the drum was taken Dribidu decided to go and see his people. As he was leaving he told them that he was only going to fetch their brothers who were behind and would come back to be their leader. He left Agalaha as the leader of the people there. When he was away some of his men came from another direction; hearing that Dribidu had settled here they wanted to come and join, but by then other lineages had occupied all the surrounding lands and so they opened another settlement far from this place. We know this to be so because we often find two separate lineages with the same name. For example, there we have Lamila[1] and again near the Congo we have Lamila. Some of the people who were lost settled at Ebi.

The majority of the people who had more cattle and other foodstuffs were then left behind. When Dribidu arrived there he found it difficult to bring them up to this place. He then told them to settle in the place where he found them. Those people again divided themselves into groups as they had settled before. After all had settled he gave to each group each type of seed and as there were many cattle there each group got enough.

As Dribidu left us under the care of Agalaha we never saw him again. He died over there[2] and we only heard stories about him. Agalaha did the same thing as Dribidu did. He had difficulty in dividing things among the different groups as their possessions were few. Those who were less respected got, for example, a bull and the others a cow. Agalaha shared his things out wisely. Those people who got bulls instead of cows were to exchange with those who received cows afterwards. For that reason some of the bulls were dotted with lime so as to be recognizable from the others. After a long time those cows were

---

[1] This story is from Maraca, in northern Lugbara.
[2] Dribidu's grave is on the top of Mount Eti, in the centre of the country.

given to every village and from village to every home. Goats and sheep were divided as well. Some of the lucky people had many cattle after they were given out and so their work was to take care of cattle. The unlucky ones lost all their cattle, and so to keep busy they had to cultivate.

(24–38)

SOMALI STORIES

Translated by B. W. Andrzejewski

The Somali language is in a period of transition. Although as yet it has no official orthography, attempts are being made to write it, and it is very likely that in the not very distant future Somali will be raised to the full status of a written language. The selection of the stories given here reflects the present position of Somali: some of the stories have been taken down by myself directly from language informants who were illiterate in their own language, while other stories have been selected from a collection of Somali texts, *Hikmad Soomaali*,[1] written by Mr. Muuse Haaji Ismaaʻiil Galaal, a pioneer in the field of Somali orthography. There are nine of these latter stories: 'The grain that escaped the pestle and mortar', 'The man who lived with the tribe of his wife', 'The reward', 'What is not honest will end badly', 'Misfortune has jaws by which it can be seized, but it has no tail', 'Broken peace cannot be mended', 'The toothless widower', 'The artful miser', and 'The soothsayer who was put to the test'.

As yet there is no tradition of written style in Somali and the artistic form of the texts of Mr. Galaal differs little from that of the texts obtained orally from my informants. The style of the Somali narrative is marked by great restraint in the use of descriptive detail and characterization, and has hardly any embellishments such as metaphors or similes. It is usually free from narrators' comments or asides and in its factual approach resembles reportage. In this respect it stands in sharp contrast to Somali alliterative poetry in which stylistic effects and imagery assume paramount importance, not infrequently at the expense of clarity and precision.

The bareness of the Somali narrative is richly compensated for, under natural conditions, by artistic effects which cannot be written down; a good narrator changes the quality of his voice when he impersonates different characters in the dialogue, while his facial expressions and his movements help the audience to reach an illusion

---

[1] *Hikmad Soomaali*, by Muuse Haaji Ismaaʻill Galaal, edited with grammatical introduction and notes by B. W. Andrzejewski (Annotated African Texts IV), O.U.P., 1956. In this book only the Somali text is given.

of reality. In the translations given here the simplicity of the Somali narrative is imitated and no attempt is made to introduce any artistic effects which are not present in the original. In fact the translation departs very little from the original with one notable exception. In the Somali narrative direct speech is always introduced by such words as 'he said' or 'they said', but these are often left out in the English version. They are repeated so frequently in Somali that if they were translated each time they would render the English version very ungainly, especially for a silent reader, even though they might be quite acceptable when read aloud by a really good actor.

When the unfamiliarity of the social background presents difficulty footnotes are provided, but they are kept to a minimum. Readers who would like to place the stories translated here in a wider context of Somali culture would do well to consult the following books: *A Pastoral Democracy*,[1] by Dr. I. M. Lewis, and *Somalia*,[2] by Dr. Enrico Cerulli.

A certain amount of Somali oral tradition has already been recorded and translated into world languages. In 1936 Edouard Duchenet published his *Histoires Somalies*[3] and in 1954 appeared *A Tree for Poverty*,[4] by Margaret Laurence, but much of the translated material is scattered throughout works on Somali grammar and in learned journals, for which bibliographical references can be found in *The Non-Bantu Languages of North-Eastern Africa*,[5] by A. N. Tucker and M. A. Bryan, and in *Hikmad Soomaali*. Among the publications listed in the bibliographies the following items may be of particular interest to the general reader: 'Somali Studien'[6] by K. Berghold; *Somali Texte und Untersuchungen zur Somali Lautlehre*,[7] by M. von Tiling; and *A Grammar of the Somali Language with Examples in Prose and Verse*,[8] by J. W. C. Kirk.

The original texts of all the stories other than those from *Hikmad Soomaali* were written down by myself under dictation or from recordings. They are as yet unpublished, but may be consulted, by arrangement, in the Departmental Library, Department of Africa, School of Oriental and African Studies, University of London.

Note that in all the Somali proper names which occur in the present stories, the letter H represents a voiceless pharyngeal fricative sound, which in the Somali original is represented by a special phonetic symbol.

---

[1] O.U.P., 1961.
[2] Istituto Poligrafico dello Stato, Rome, 1959, 2 vols.
[3] Larose Éditeurs, Paris, 1936.
[4] Published for the Somaliland Protectorate by The Eagle Press, Nairobi, 1954.
[5] *Handbook of African Languages*, Part III, O.U.P., 1956.
[6] *Vienna Oriental Journal* (*Wiener Zeitschrift für die Kunde des Morgenlandes*), vol. xiii (1899), 123–98.
[7] Berlin, 1925, Achtes Beiheft zur Zeitschrift für Eingeborenen Sprachen.
[8] Cambridge University Press, 1905.

24

The Grain that Escaped the Pestle and Mortar

THERE was an old woman who had only one son. One day the boy decided to join a raiding expedition, and the woman, terrified—for he was her only son—said to him, 'My son, stay at home!' But the boy refused, saying, 'Nothing will keep me away from the young men of my age who are joining the raid!' She begged and begged him to stay, leaving nothing unsaid in her pleas, but he still refused.

At last she said, 'Well, then, I shall bless you. Give me the hem of your garment.' He lifted it up, and she poured sand into it, saying, 'May God turn you into the grain that escaped the pestle and mortar!'

The raiding party set out, the boy with them, but in their settlement there were spies of the tribe which was to be attacked, so that it was forewarned and ready. The raiders reached the place next morning after a long journey, and unaware of the preparation, attacked the settlement. But they were ambushed by the other tribe, and after many hours of fighting at the end of the day all the attackers had been killed except for the young boy, who was captured.

Then a certain man took him under his protection, and, giving the boy provisions for the journey, sent him back to his own people. Thus, out of the whole raiding party, only the young boy escaped.

25

The Man who Lived with the Tribe of His Wife

THERE was a man, it is said, who lived with the tribe of his wife. One day he said to his wife, 'We are moving away—tell your people.' So she told her people and they gave him the customary gifts and returned to him a part of the bridewealth.

Then this man who had been living with his wife's tribe moved away with his family and his wife, and after he had walked all day he set up camp in a certain place. Then he said to his wife, 'Woman, there is a matter I have to discuss with the people whom we left, and I am going back to them. Pen the animals and wait for me.'

So he went back, and when he reached the village in the late evening he sat down in the clearing by the huts, intending to eavesdrop. The people were gossiping about him and someone said: 'Well, let us all give our opinion of that man who stayed with our tribe for such a long time!'

'He was a good man,' said one.

'By God, he was a brave man,' said another.

'By God, he was a generous man.'

'By God, he looked after the animals well.'

'By God, he had some knowledge of men.'

The whole village praised him, and all the time the man was listening. There was a pause, and then a young girl, still with a tuft of hair on her head,[1] spoke, 'But I know something about him that was bad!'

'What was it?' the people asked.

'He didn't go far enough away from the huts when he urinated!' At this the whole village burst into laughter, but the eavesdropper was so angry that he stood up and said to them, 'Well, by God, I have moved far enough away now!' to the great astonishment of the whole village.

26

The Reward

THERE was once a band of warriors who went on a raiding expedition, and when they were about half-way on their journey they sent out scouts. The scouts came to a settlement which the band planned to attack, and being hungry they pretended to be travellers. But the people of the place went to sleep without offering them hospitality.

In the morning the hungry scouts trudged away, and in the late afternoon they came to another settlement not very far from the first. Then one of the men of that place saw that they were

---

[1] Among some Somali tribes this is a sign of not yet being of marriageable age.

very hungry, so he took them with him and led them to his home, where he gave them milk. He did not know that they were scouts.

When they had drunk the milk he said to them, 'Men, I gave you that milk out of fear of the Lord and in the expectation of reward from men and protection for my home!' Then, taking the milk-vessel, he went away.

The scouts also left the place, and when they had been travelling for some time, one of them said, 'Did you hear what the man said?'

'Yes,' was the reply.

'And how shall we reward him?'

'Let us guide the band away from his settlement!'

They agreed on this, and when they got back to the band they said: 'There are two settlements there. The one which is farther away has not many camels, so let us rob the nearer one.' Then they looted the nearer one and killed many men.

27

'What is not honest will end badly'

I⊤ is said that once a Lion, a Snake, a Thorny Fence, Fire, Flood, Deceit, and Honesty owned a she-camel together. One day Deceit, planning to take away the she-camel from all the others, went to the Snake and said, 'Now, in the first place, this man called Lion is indeed very great, and one day he will kill us all. Why don't we simply catch him and kill him ourselves?'

'How shall we catch him?' asked the Snake.

'Well, you are a small snake; you can creep into the thick part of the Fence, near the gate, and lie in wait for the Lion as he comes home in the evening. Then bite him suddenly, and get back again into the Fence!'

So when the Lion returned home at night, the Snake bit him and then quickly got into the Fence. The Lion died, and the Snake, being now a man guilty of bloodshed, stayed hidden in the Fence.

Then Deceit went to Fire and said, 'Listen, Fire! Surely this Snake who killed the Lion will not leave us alone: tomorrow he will kill us all! What shall we do?' 'Well, I don't know,' replied Fire: 'What do you think?' Said Deceit, 'You are Fire— burn the Snake in the Fence!' So Fire agreed, and burnt the Fence and the Snake together.

Then Deceit went to Flood and said, 'Listen! This Fire which completely burnt the land will surely not leave us in peace. Extinguish him!' So Flood extinguished Fire, and then only Deceit and Honesty were left. Deceit said, 'Listen, let us move on with the she-camel', so they drove her along, and on their way they climbed a hill.[1] Deceit suggested that they milk the she-camel, and they filled a vessel with the milk. Then she put some froth from the milk on the back of the she-camel's knee, and said, 'Now, Honesty, I dare you to lick that froth on the back of the she-camel's knee!' But Honesty realized that Deceit was hoping that the she-camel would kick her. Then Deceit, to encourage her, said, 'Now, watch! I am going to lick it!' and she sprang forward to do it. Then the she-camel kicked her and split her belly open, leaving Honesty as the sole owner of the she-camel.

28

The Two Tricksters

IT is said that once two thieves saw a traveller who was driving a ram and carrying a vessel of ghee, and they consulted together as to how they should rob him. One of them said, 'I shall play a trick on him', and sitting down by the side of the road along which the traveller was passing, he began to cry out, 'Listen, Moslems!' The traveller came towards him and said, 'Why are you shouting?'

'I am blind,' said the thief, 'and I am seeking someone who would take me into the town!'

'I shall lead you,' replied the traveller, 'and you will take the rope and lead the ram.'

The thief agreed, but when they had been walking for a while he said, 'Listen to me! There is no animal on the rope which I am holding!'

[1] Flood, naturally, could not climb the hill and was left behind.

'When did the rope get loosened?' asked the traveller.

'Just now!' was the reply.

'I shall go back along the road,' said the traveller, 'Hold the vessel of ghee for me.' He went back, while the thief ran away with the vessel. Thus the traveller saw no more of his ram and his ghee.

29

'Misfortune has jaws by which it can be seized, but it has no tail'

Two small girls who were looking after the sheep and goats were one day boasting to each other about whose father was better.

'My father is the greatest of all men!' said one.

'What, do you think he is greater than my father?' replied the other.

'Yes!' said the first.

'In what way is he greater than my father, then?'

'Why, in his manly deeds: when the ground cracks open, my father can mend it!'

The other girl was astonished, and kept quiet for a while. Then she said, 'Well, if your father can mend the ground when it cracks open, he is a clever man. But as for me—in the place where my father is standing the ground does not crack at all!'

30

The Man who fell in Love with a Sultan's Daughter

ONCE there was a sultan who had one daughter who was very beautiful, and no other children. She fell in love with a certain man, and when some time later the sultan found out about it he employed an old woman to spy on them, saying to her, 'Tell me at what time he visits her.'

The old woman told the sultan who the man was and at what time he used to visit the girl, and when he heard this he sent soldiers to arrest the man. When the soldiers brought him to the sultan, he passed sentence on him that he should be buried in a pit, except for his head, which was to be left above the ground. Then he would be stoned to death.

'When you have buried him in a pit, all except his head,' the sultan said to the soldiers, 'do not kill him, but leave him for two days. Let him stay there! Then on the third day, in the evening, knock off his head with stones!'

Before the third day came an old woman passed by near the man whose head was sticking out of the pit.

'What has happened to you?' she asked.

'I am a hunchback,' he replied, 'and I was told that if I buried myself in the sand and people put heavy sand on my back, my hump would disappear!'

Now the old woman was a hunchback herself.

'If I do the same, shall I be healed and will my hump disappear?'

'Yes,' he replied, 'I have been healed, and if you want me to come out of the pit, dig me out of the sand. Then when you get into the pit I shall cover you up with sand. Just stay in it for two days and after that time I shall come to you. This evening I shall drive the sheep and goats home for you.'

'All right.'

'Take a piece of cloth and tie a turban on your head,' he said to her.

'My hands are buried. Tie it for me!'

So he did, and soon after he left her the soldiers sent by the sultan came with stones and began to hit the woman with them until they knocked off her head.

When the old woman was dead they said, 'Now that he is dead let us take him out of the pit so that he may be buried.'

When they took the body out they saw that it was not the man but an old hunchbacked woman. They went back to the sultan and told him what had happened.

The sultan laughed, and said, 'Leave him in peace, he has had good luck! Call him to me!'

They went to look for him. When they had found him and he had told them about his trick, the sultan said to him, 'You are a clever man, and I want you to work for me!'

After the man had worked for him for a while, the sultan gave him his daughter in marriage and made him his chancellor.

Sheikh Uwees¹ and the Man who prayed over his Grave

ONCE a certain man lost his animals, and people told him to
go to the tomb of Sheikh Uwees. 'When you get there,' they said,
'weep and ask the sheikh for help. You will get your animals
back, that is certain!'

The man did this and when he got to the place he begged the
sheikh for help, wept and then went to sleep over the tomb. At
midnight one of the sheikh's disciples appeared to the man
sleeping over the tomb and spoke to him. The man woke up,
and when the disciple asked him what had happened to him, he
said, 'Some time ago I lost many animals—sheep, goats, and
cattle—and I searched for them but could not find them. Now
I have come to ask the sheikh for my animals, and on my way
to the tomb, I prayed to him for help as I walked along. In this
way I made my journey.'

'The sheikh says to you,' said the disciple, 'that you should
now go to sleep. When the dawn comes, the animals which you
lost will come to the tomb, and then you can drive them away.'

The man went to sleep, and when the dawn came, to his great
joy he saw the animals. Then he slaughtered two animals from
his herd of cattle as a pilgrimage offering in honour of the
sheikh.

32

'Broken peace cannot be mended'

ONCE there was a man who settled in an encampment in which
he discovered there was a snake. However, it did no harm to
anyone, and every day it used to pass to and fro among the
children and animals without hurting them.

---

¹ Sheikh Uwees is regarded as a saint and miracles are attributed to him. He was
a contemporary of Muhammed 'Abdille Hasan ('The Mad Mullah') and was
killed in 1909 at Biyoley. His grave is a place of pilgrimage. The sheikh had many
disciples and it is implied that the one who appeared to the man in the story was a
spirit sent from the other world. For further information about Sheikh Uwees (also
spelt Awes and Uways) readers are referred to Enrico Cerulli's article 'Note sul
movimento musulmano nella Somalia', *Rivista degli Studi Orientali*, x (1923), 1–36,
reprinted in his *Somalia*.

One day the man reflected on this, and said to himself, 'Why not kill this snake so that it may not bite any of your animals or children?' He went to the snake, which was sleeping in a tree-trunk, and said to himself, 'Hit it in the neck with the sword!' But he missed it and the sword hit the trunk of the tree, while the snake woke up and fled away into a hole.

At night, when the people were asleep, the snake came out and bit the first-born son of the man, and the son died. In the morning the man went to the snake and said, 'Snake, let us make a pact and leave each other in peace!'

But the snake replied, 'Man, in the past we did live in peace and you broke it. Now, as long as I see the mark of the sword on the tree-trunk, and as long as you see the grave of your son, no pact can be made between us. Let us part!'

33

The Toothless Widower

ONCE there was a man who was toothless. He had a good wife and she used to chew the food for him, but then she died and was buried. Even after everyone had departed from her grave, her husband stayed behind and wept over it, and as he wept the sun set and he spent the night there. Next day at dawn an old man was passing by the place and saw the man who was sitting over the grave. He walked towards him, greeted him, and asked him for the news.

The man whose wife had died told him what had happened, 'My wife died yesterday and she was buried here.'

'Your wife has died? But what makes you sit here, over her grave?'

'If my wife is dead can I hope for anything more from life? Let my soul depart here, in this place!'

'She was, perhaps, a good wife?'

'Yes!' the man answered.

'And have you any other wife?'

'No!'

'Why was it that you loved this wife of whom you have been bereaved?'

'Because I am toothless, and she used to chew the food for me.'
'And you think that another woman would not do the same?'
'No!'

Then the old man said, 'Hasten away now and marry another wife. It may be that you will find a better one!'

The man whose wife had died bowed himself down, perplexed. 'Why not do that?' he asked himself. Then he said to the old man, 'You are right; I will do it.'

Then he married another wife. She did not chew the food for him, but ground it, and to his surprise the food which was chewed and the food which was ground were not the same, for in the food which was ground there was more taste and nourishment.

One morning he went out, carrying fire, to the grave of the wife who had died.[1] He met on the way the old man who had advised him.

'Where are you taking the fire?' the old man asked.

'Recently a wife of mine died, and I am going to desecrate her grave by burning it,' was the answer.

'Why?'

'She used to cheat me!'

'How did she used to cheat you?'

'I am toothless and she used to chew the food for me, but after she had swallowed all the tasty juices the food which she gave me was without savour!'

'When did you find this out?'

'Just now.'

'And how did you find out?'

'I married another wife, and she did not do me the disservice of chewing the food, but ground it instead.'

'Now, do you remember me?' asked the old man.

'No,' the other man replied.

'I am the man who gave you some advice the other day when you were weeping over the grave, and who said to you "Marry another wife". Now I shall say this to you, the wife who used to chew the food for you, because you were toothless, was not a bad

---

[1] Here the story makes use, in a literal fashion, of a common phrase 'If I do so, burn my grave', meaning 'If I do so, do not honour my memory when I die'. Somalis do not, indeed could not, literally 'burn graves', taking into account the fact that graves are made of earth and stones. This device of using metaphorical expressions literally is not uncommon in Somali oral traditions.

wife; do not burn her grave, having found a better wife, but go
and pray for her, and throw away the fire. Remember that
among the children of Adam, however good a person may be,
there is always to be found someone who is even better!'

34

Sheikh 'Abdi Rahmaan Binu Haashin[1] and the Crocodile

THE sheikh used to carry a stick with him and one day he put it
in the river, climbed on it, and the stick moved along with him.
When he reached the middle of the river a crocodile caught him.

'Crocodile,' said the sheikh, 'why have you bitten me?'

'I have bitten you because when God was creating the world
he assigned to me all that comes into the river, and so I have
bitten you.'

'Let us go to the other bank of the river and you will see the
power of grace which is in me!' said the sheikh.

The sheikh crossed the river and the crocodile went with him.
Then the sheikh spat on the crocodile and it turned into a fish.
The sheikh then caught it and ate it.

35

Fiqishinni, the 'Bee-Scribe'[2]

FIQISHINNI, it is said, was an exiled scribe, and even now no
one knows where he came from. He was a learned man in the
faith of Islam, and once when he was inside a cave, praying
aloud and reading the Qur'ān, a girl who was looking after
sheep and goats heard something that sounded like the noise of
bees near the cave.

As she approached the cave, thinking that there were bees
buzzing there, she saw a man inside, reading the Qur'ān. She

---

[1] This man of religion, reputed for his saintliness, was one of the disciples of
Sheikh Uwees.

[2] The eponymous ancestor of the tribal group called Reer Fiqishinni in the
northern part of the Somali Republic. It would be very difficult to establish when
he lived.

stooped down, and as she was looking in at the scribe reading there, he also saw her.

'Peace be on you!' she said.

'And peace be on you!' he answered.

'What are you doing there?'

'My dear, I am praying aloud!'

'Will you come with me?' she said. 'Let me give you shelter for the night in our settlement.'

'My dear,' he replied, 'I shall come with you. When you drive the sheep and goats home in the afternoon come here for me.'

'All right.'

So they went home together. After he had stayed for the night in her settlement, he decided to leave in the morning. The girl came to him and said, 'Scribe, I want you to stay with us and teach me the Qur'ān.'

'What fee will you give me for this?'

'Marry me!' she said.

'My dear, will you be able to cope with a man who has a large stomach, a large penis, and large feet?'

'Yes!'

'Now, tell me how you will be able to do this.'

'To a man with a large stomach,' she replied, 'one gives enough food to satisfy it, and I shall give you enough. About a man who has a large penis I shall say this, the mouth of a vessel is always larger than the stopper. As for a man with large feet, one asks him to put his foot on a piece of leather and one cuts out soles for his sandals of the right size.'

'You have found the right answer to my test of wisdom,' said the scribe. 'I shall do what you tell me: I shall marry you.'

Then they married each other and Fiquishinni became the ancestor of the Fiquishinni Tribe.

36

The Artful Miser

THERE was once a man, it is said, who neither gave people anything nor yet refused them. By deceit and trickery he avoided giving anything to anyone, yet everybody went away from him happy to have received nothing.

After some time people began to gossip about him, and one day four mullahs heard the talk and said, 'Let us question this man about whom the people are gossiping. If he is a miser, we will admonish him, saying, "Oh man, abandon this miserliness lest you be punished in the other world!" But if the people are telling lies, we will defend him against them.'

So they went to the man, and said, 'First of all, are you the man who is a miser and about whom the people are gossiping?'

He replied, 'Brothers, do you listen to such people? If they say that I am a miser, take no notice! I shall give you whatever you want!'

The mullahs looked at each other, and said, 'Maybe the people are telling lies! Let us sit down and see what he will do.'

Then the man said to his wife, who understood well his way of speaking, 'My dear, spread the Dogskin Mat[1] for these men in the Polluted Enclosure!' When the men heard these words they looked at each other in astonishment. The wife put a skin in an enclosure near by, and then while the men were still not sure what to make of the matter, the man said again, 'My dear, take some donkey's dung and clean the milk-vessel called Dirty-edged One with it!' Again the mullahs turned to each other in amazement when they heard the evil name of the vessel and with what it was to be cleaned.

She took the vessel away and cleaned it with something which the men did not see, then brought it back to her husband, saying 'The milk-vessel is ready.' He said, 'Milk for these men the cow So-and-so which I looted from the orphans!' At this the mullahs departed, saying, 'Away with you, you devil, we shall not eat your food!' The man ran after them and said, 'Brothers, do not go away! Come and find out what I shall give you!' But the mullahs refused, and swore not to have anything to do with his household or any of his things, without investigating any further!

[1] It is the Somali custom in the nomadic interior to give proper names to various utensils and objects in the household. Normally such names are pleasant or indifferent, but the miser in the story invented special names which would suggest something disgusting or abhorrent to a pious Moslem. The wet parts of a dog are considered to be ritually unclean, and the name Dirty-edged One in the original suggests that the dirt in question is from human genitals. To drink the milk of a cow stolen from an orphan would be considered as no less odious.

Garaad Muhammed[1]

WHEN Muhammed was a small boy his father died, and being an orphan he went to live with his stepmother, the widow of his father, and she looked after him. His own mother had died before his father. His stepmother was the daughter of Muumin, the Ugaas of the Ogaden. She, the daughter of Muumin, was married, after she was widowed, by 'Adduur 'Ali, who was Muhammed's uncle. 'Adduur 'Ali was the brother of Muhammed's father, Garaad Mahamuud, and he also had another brother called Samakaab.

Now Samakaab said to 'Adduur 'Ali, 'Listen, man. Our brother the Garaad is dead, and the children he left are certainly too young to take his place as Garaad. You must either take it yourself, or marry the young woman who is his widow.'

'I shall think about it and take counsel,' replied 'Adduur 'Ali. He went to the woman and told her about the matter, and she said, 'Do not give any answer to Samakaab 'Ali until you hear further news from me.' Then she called young Muhammed and said to him, 'Listen, boy. People are planning to prevent you from becoming Garaad!'

'What do you think I should do?' he asked.

'If you do what I tell you, you will become Garaad!'

'What must I do?'

'What you must do is this: every day, go to the assembly, put on good clothes, and do what your father used to do when he went to the assembly. When people ask you for something, grant it to them, and then tell me and I will pay whatever you have granted.'

When for some time the boy had granted whatever was asked of him, the people said, 'Listen, men! This one is even more noble than his father!' He soon gained a great reputation, all

---

[1] *Garaad* and *ugaas* (also spelt *gerad* and *ugas*) are Somali names for chieftains or sultans. All the men in this story are connected with the tribal history of the Las Anod Province of the Somali Republic. It would not be easy to date the events described or even establish their authenticity. For further information see I. M. Lewis, *A Pastoral Democracy*.

the people loving him and planning that he should be made Garaad.

When matters had been like this for some time, Samakaab 'Ali said, 'Listen, 'Adduur. Did I not say to you, either take the kingdom for yourself, or marry the widow?' 'Adduur 'Ali then said, 'I shall marry the widow,' and Samakaab said, 'And I shall take the kingdom for myself.'

'Adduur 'Ali and the woman he was going to marry, the stepmother of Muhammed, wanted to outwit Samakaab 'Ali by having young Muhammed, the rightful heir, made Garaad. To this end they did all they could to spread Muhammed's good reputation all over the country and to blacken the character of Samakaab 'Ali, who wanted to deprive him of his kingdom. When they were satisfied that their design had gone well, and that the people did not want Samakaab 'Ali, but Muhammed, who was young, to become Garaad, they one day called an assembly. They told Samakaab 'Ali, 'You must come to the assembly because the question of Garaad-making will be dealt with.'

All the people gathered for the assembly, and while Samakaab 'Ali was saying to himself, 'It is you whom they are going to make Garaad!', a man was chosen to perform the ceremony and this man got up. The people had agreed together that Samakaab should not know that Muhammed was going to be made Garaad until the moment of crowning, and now the man who was to bestow the crown stood with it in his hands. He said three times: 'Let him be the Garaad!' and, while Samakaab 'Ali was still thinking mistakenly that it was he who would be crowned, the man put the crown on Muhammed. All the people cried: 'Accept him as your Garaad!' but Samakaab 'Ali, dumbfounded, left the assembly in anger.

38

The Soothsayer who was put to the Test

THERE was a man, it is said, who was a soothsayer, and he had a great knowledge of the art of divining from the beads of a rosary.[1] The people loved him, and everyone who was

[1] The Somalis use a form of divination called *faal*, which consists of counting the

concerned about something came to him saying: 'Divine for me!' and this he did. The Somali soothsayers, when they divine, do not say that this or that will happen; they say, 'This or that used to be said.'

So, all the people loving the soothsayer and coming to him from every part, he became famous in the whole country, and after some time news of him reached the sultan. Hearing how the people praised him, the sultan decided to find out to what extent his knowledge was genuine, and one day, as the people were talking about the soothsayer in the assembly, the sultan spoke: 'In my opinion, that man knows nothing!'

'Sultan!' the people cried, 'No one has ever seen a man who is wiser than he!'

'Then find him for me, and I shall ask him a question. If he answers it—well, he is a man who knows something and I shall reward him. But if not—he is a deceiver and I shall cut off his head!'

They were frightened, and said, 'Sultan, he is a good man, do not kill him!'

'Find him for me!' the sultan repeated, and men were sent out with orders to bring the soothsayer to the assembly within seven days. After the messengers who were sent out had been looking for him for some time, at last one day they found him and brought him to the sultan, who then called an assembly. When the people had gathered, the sultan said, 'Is it you who said that you knew many things?'

The soothsayer, thinking that he might have been accused of some offence, began to deny his knowledge, but the sultan laughed and said, 'Leave your excuses! Word has spread over the country that So-and-so has great knowledge, and today you must know the answer to the question I will ask you.'

The man was unable to speak, and bowed his head in apprehension.

'Sultan,' cried the men who were sitting in the assembly,

---

beads of a rosary. The diviner takes the rosary and counts the beads with both hands simultaneously, starting at random at any two points. At the end either one or two beads are left, and he repeats this procedure four times. The combination of four results makes up a set, called *min*. Each set is considered to give a particular horoscope, except that one of them is an empty *min* and portends nothing. When the *faal* predicts misfortune the diviner performs certain actions to avert it, which may even include cutting his finger.

'we know this man; he is a man of wisdom. Ask him some-thing.'

The sultan turned angrily to the soothsayer and said, 'So you tell other people what they ask you, yet refuse to do this for me!'

'Sultan, I know nothing.'

'I command you to tell me what the next year will be like. Make your divination from the beads of your rosary, or from plants, and if what you say comes true, I shall make you wealthy. But I tell you that if you divine falsely, I shall cut off your head.'

So now the soothsayer took his rosary and began counting the beads and calculating the horoscopes. Many times he did this, counting and calculating, counting and calculating, but alas, every horoscope predicted misfortune coming upon himself. Seized with fright, he threw the rosary on the ground, abused it, cursed it, even jumped on it, then bit it and broke off two beads. In his fury, he pulled out his dagger, and as he did so he cut his finger. Blood began to pour from the wound, shalala-lalahh! Then all the people who were in the assembly were alarmed and said, 'He has gone mad—beware of his dagger!'

'Tell us what this means,' demanded the sultan.

'Sultan, none of the horoscopes answered my question and each of them told me of misfortune coming upon me, so I was warding it off.'

'Work out another horoscope, then.'

So he turned the beads, and when he saw the result, he said, 'Sultan, there is a horoscope here.' The sultan said, 'What does it portend?' Then the soothsayer turned the beads again and a horoscope predicting a journey came out. He was so frightened that the rosary fell from his hands, and the sultan said, 'What happened?'

The soothsayer opened his mouth but could not speak. When the sultan chided him, saying, 'Tell me the result!' he could only stammer, 'Sultan . . . O Sultan!' The sultan became angry at his silence and moved toward him, saying, 'Speak!'

'O Sultan, the power of prediction has left me!'

The sultan angrily dismissed him, saying, 'In seven days I shall want the answer to my question,' and then left the place.

The assembly dispersed, but the soothsayer still sat there frightened and unable to move. After sitting for some time after the people had gone, once again he took his rosary and counted the beads; alas, once again the numbers meant nothing. He threw down the rosary, cursing it, wiping out his calculations on the sand, and began to walk up and down. He was half out of his mind with fear, and raved and babbled to himself as he walked. But after a while the first shock lessened and he began to come to his senses, saying to himself, 'You fool, this is not the way! Calm down, abandon fear and turn your attention to the counting of your beads!'

So he set to once more. But again and again the numbers were meaningless and empty, and soon he realized the seriousness of his situation. 'What will you do?' he asked himself.

He thought and thought, and at last he stood up and said, 'O God, I take a vow that until I find the answer for the sultan I shall not sleep, I shall not eat, I shall not speak to anybody nor go anywhere where there are people.'

So he went into an uninhabited region overgrown with bush, and walked for some time, stopping to count the beads in vain, cutting plants and divining from them, and calculating the horoscopes in the sand. When everything had failed, and he was very tired, he laid his prayer mat under a shady tree and sat down, saying to himself, 'Well, if death has to come to you, let it come to you under this tree. Sit down!'

For several nights he slept there. Every day, before dawn and after sunset when the sky is red, he counted the beads of his rosary and made a divination to see whether his power of prediction would come back to him, but always the numbers were meaningless.

When only one day was left of the appointed time, he was in despair and determined that his soul should leave his body there; but suddenly, from out of the shadow of the tree-trunk under which he was lying there appeared an old and mighty serpent. Unable to control himself he leaped up and spear in hand he ran a few steps and then turned to face it. 'Beware of this beast!' he said to himself

The serpent coiled itself and raising its head, spoke to him: 'Why have you run away?'

'I am afraid of you and I am on my guard.'

'Don't be afraid of me, for I have come here in order to talk to you, not to harm you.'

The soothsayer was not a man who was used to seeing serpents which talk, and he was so astonished that he did not know what to say and put his hands to his cheeks in amazement.

'I shall not believe you,' he said after a few moments, 'for no one has yet seen a serpent which speaks!'

'If you have not seen one before, see it now!' the serpent laughed.

'I shall not trust you.'

'Let us make a pact,' said the serpent.

'Very well,' agreed the soothsayer, after a long silence.

Then, with the horny tip of its tail, the serpent cut a circle on the ground, like a camel enclosure. Placing itself in the middle, it swore an oath: 'I swear by God that I shall not harm you unless you force me to it.' Then it came out of the circle and the man went in and swore the same oath. After this was done they asked each other many questions and exchanged news. At last the serpent asked, 'What has brought you from your country and what are you looking for in this land of ours?'

'Our sultan', explained the soothsayer, 'asked me to tell him what the coming year will be. But the power of prediction left me and I came into this bush country, where I went on divining.'

'And have you found the answer for the sultan?'

'No.'

'What will you give me if I tell you the answer?'

'I will give you whatever you want.'

'If you answer the question what will the sultan give you?'

'Many animals.'

'If I tell you what the coming year will be, will you give me half of them?'

'By God Almighty, no, I shall bring you everything!'

'Don't bring me everything. Take half for yourself and bring me the other half.'

'Very well.'

'This is what you will say to the sultan.[1]

"I have deciphered the secrets of the time which is coming; listen to me. It is the time of the evil deeds of the djinns, and eight years[2] have passed since the deeds of

[1] The serpent's oracles in this story are in the form of alliterative poems, which are rendered here in prose.

[2] There is a belief current among the Somalis that events tend to repeat themselves every eight years.

Iblis.[1] These are portents which tell of a wife putting on a mourning head-dress, and of brave men slaughtered, and of flocks which will be looted, and of sturdy warriors at whose bodies the birds of prey will peck, and of evil.

"Men made busy preparations for war: their rusty spears they have sharpened for the battle, their fatted horses they have harnessed for an affray, on the waterskin which had become dry they fastened a handle, against thirst.

"Whether you sleep or run away, or take out your sword from the scabbard against it, soon fierce men (against the very dust which they will raise, you will say your prayers in awe) will be locked in combat." '

When the soothsayer had heard the whole *geeraar*-song,[2] he blessed the serpent and hurried away.

Meanwhile, in the settlement, people were gathered in the assembly. Some men said, 'The appointed time has elapsed, where is the man?' and again, 'Maybe he could not find the answer and ran away.' Said others, 'Today is the last day, but let us wait till the evening.'

In the late afternoon they saw in the distance a column of dust, and as they were asking each other what it could be, they made out that it was a man who was running and singing a *geeraar*-song. It was the soothsayer, lean, with his lips cracked with thirst and his eyes sunken. Indeed, it was a man who has not tasted anything for seven days, and at whose condition you would be astonished.

The people were amazed. As was the custom, first of all he shook hands with the sultan, and then, with the people listening attentively and wondering what he would say, he recited the *geeraar*. At the end, everyone was filled with great joy and people rushed to shake his hand.

'Escort him to my house and kill for him a fatted she-camel,' ordered the sultan. Then he sent men among the people telling them that there would be assembly eight days later at which everyone must be present; this was done, and the whole tribe assembled, not one man being absent.

The sultan gave them the news, 'The time which is coming is a time of war. Let every man fatten his horse, keep his

[1] Lit. 'the eighth anniversary of Iblis'—Iblis being the prince of the evil genii.
[2] *Geeraar* is a type of alliterative poem, usually chanted.

weapons near and sharpen his spears. Everybody must keep
strong horses at hand, and while this time of war lasts, every
day is a day of assembly for all of us!'

So every day the men assembled and prepared their weapons;
patrols were sent out and every man lived away from his home.
Then one day there came a message from one of the patrols:
'Arise, we are attacked!' Men seized their horses and took up
their weapons, and in the early morning when the animals
had gone out to graze, a motley band of marauders attacked
the settlement. But the defenders, being prepared and forewarned, ambushed and defeated the raiding party. They forced
it to retreat and drove it away into a distant place.

Later another band attacked the settlement, and again was
defeated. It was a time of war and at every sunset and every
dawn men entered into battle; the world was in a state of chaos
and no one either rested or slept. But the tribe defeated every
attack and whatever expedition they themselves sent was vic-
torious, for they were well prepared.

Thus the year ended. The war destroyed every tribe among
all the people, except for the tribe of the sultan, and one day
the sultan called them all together, talked to them, and praised
them. Then he called for the soothsayer and said, 'You have
done well, and I am pleased with you. Now take for yourself
that herd of camels, that herd of sheep and goats, that herd of
cattle, and that herd of horses. It is your reward.'

The man was delighted, shook hands with the sultan, and
drove away the animals in front of him. After he had gone
some way, he remembered the bargain which he had made
with the serpent, so he went among the animals saying to
himself, 'Take the serpent his share.' But as he looked carefully
at them and realized what fine animals they were, the vein of
thriftiness moved within him. 'Are you giving animals of that
beauty to a serpent?' he asked himself. 'Fool begotten by a
fool! Instead of giving animals to a dangerous beast, just take
your sword and kill it, once and for all!'

He drew his sword out of the scabbard, and handing over the
animals to his servants to drive on for him, he went to find the
serpent. When he came upon it, it was sleeping, and he raised
his sword, meaning to cut off its head. But just as he was about
to strike—I don't know what it had noticed, but it ran away

and escaped into the thick forest. The sword fell with a thud on the place where the serpent's head had been.

'May your hand wither!' cried the soothsayer to himself. 'The beast will jump towards you and in its fury will cut you into two pieces. Run away!' So he ran and ran, and at last he reached the servants who were with the animals. In a panic, he made them run too, and they drove the animals away from danger to a safe place.

After he had stayed in his home for some time, resting and enjoying himself, one day men came to him saying that the sultan had sent them for him.

'Why does he want me?' the soothsayer asked the messengers.

'We don't know,' was their reply.

He shook his head with apprehension and sat for a while in silence, asking himself why the sultan could want him. Then, 'Let us go,' he said, and followed the men.

After walking for some time they came to the sultan who was sitting in the assembly. He was pleased, and calling the soothsayer, shook hands with him and asked him the news. Then he said, 'I have called you because it was you who saved us last year and told us what the year would be. Now tell us about this year!'

The soothsayer was seized with fright and bowed his head.

'This is why you called me?' he said.

'Yes.'

'But, sultan, has not the power of prediction left me?'

'God forbid! It has not left you—it was you who knew about the past year. Don't say things which no one will accept from you. As you did last year, go away for seven days and then tell us what the year which is coming will be like. And our previous arrangement will stand!'

The soothsayer realized what a plight he was in, and after the assembly dispersed he still sat there perplexed, wondering what to do. He stayed there till the dawn came, then he said to himself: 'Why don't you go to the serpent, contrite and apologetic, and tell him how remorseful and ashamed you are of what you did to him? Why don't you tell him that you are in the same trouble as before, and ask him to get you out of it?'

He got up at once and hastened to the serpent, which was lying in the old place. Reproaching himself and weeping, he said to it, 'O serpent, I have used you ill, I have done you a great injury and I have broken the pledge given to you. Forgive me! Today I am once again in a great difficulty—get me out of it!'

The serpent laughed, gahgah, gahgah.

'Listen, O man! You have done your part. It was by God's decree that I survived, for you left nothing undone in your attempt to kill me. Nevertheless, as the rain does not come unless there are some creatures who are more forgiving than others, for God's sake I shall help you. Listen to me:

'O diviner! Mankind has been preordained to be the cause of woe to the world. You it was who invented the slaughter of each other, and the word 'stab'! The fire you have kindled will kill a great part of creation. When you are defenceless you are fond of friendship and mutual help, but for the man with whom you were friendly when you were pressed by need you do not do anything when you have achieved your aim. You have broken the covenant into which you entered, and the old pact. The evil deeds of the son of Adam will destroy the world. What you say with your lips you do not mean with your heart!

'I rescued you from the trap when you were in dire straits, and when I expected some reward and profit I got from you, you fool, a blow from your hilt-furnished sword. With the sound of the sword and the cloud of dust which harmed my head, with the fear in which I fled, and with the leaps I made, dashing myself against the euphorbia trees, and with stumbling, my ears became deaf. Your trickling tear, your leanness, your entreaty which touched my flesh, and those djinn-like supplications, were what deceived me before. Today, now I am forewarned, do not expect me to confide in you: the trust which you seek from me has fallen into a very deep hole. For God's sake I shall tell you that you are an evildoer—no doubt you have many times oppressed weak men and orphans—and in my view you are paying for the injustice which you committed and settling an old debt.

'Tell the sultan who sent you that a wasting drought will

come. Tell him that the *dihi*, *maajeen*, and *duur*[1] grass
will wither away altogether. Tell him that of the groves
and of the great trees standing alone, some will die. Tell
him that the running streams, the shallow wells, the ponds
and the valleys will become waterless. Tell him that all
the weak and poor and all the flocks will perish. Tell him
that the strong camels and black-headed sheep will remain.
Tell him that men who are enterprising and industrious
will survive.'

The soothsayer was delighted, and became so confused with
joy that he gaily turned twice around. Then he said, 'Well,
Serpent, I fully realize what it was I did to you, and I recognize
the debt of gratitude I owe you. Believe me, I shall not again
do what I did, and in fact, I shall bring to you all that I am
given.'

'Well, we shall see,' replied the serpent.

The soothsayer set off in a great hurry, and after some time
he came to the assembly. He recited the poem and when he had
finished, the people ran towards him and lifted him from the
ground in their joy. The sultan, very pleased, got up, shook
hands with him, patted his head and blessed him. Then the
people paid him great honour, entertained him, and made a
riding display for him.

Next day the sultan assembled his tribe. 'It has been foretold
for us that a time of drought is approaching. Everyone must
store away something for himself,' he told them. So every man
made a storage place with racks, on which he placed such food
as would keep.

After some months the drought began. The autumn rains
did not come and there was no rain during the following spring.
All over the country clouds of dust were blown about by the
wind, the land became bare, the trees withered, the ponds dried
up, and all the shallow wells and water-holes were exhausted,
except for the deep spring-fed wells. Then all those animals
which cannot live for a long time without water, and all the
animals with horns, died, and no livestock could be found

---

[1] Three different types of grass eaten by domestic animals. For their botanical
identification see the entries *dihi*, *dihe*, *machen*, *dur* and *durr* in P. E. Glover's *Pro-
visional Check-list of British and Italian Somaliland Trees, Shrubs and Herbs*, London,
1947, Crown Agents for the Colonies.

except for the big strong camels. Other people were not prepared for the drought and they and their animals perished, but
the sultan and his tribe turned to their stores and survived the
hard times.

One day the sultan called the soothsayer, and again gave
him many animals. Rejoicing, he drove them away, but as they
were travelling along the road, he remembered the agreement
which he and the serpent had made. Stopping the animals, he
sat down, perplexed, and drew lines on the ground while he
thought and thought. Then, as he again took stock of the
animals grazing near by the vein of the love of wealth (which is
an evil passion) began to stir in him.

'Are you going to take those animals to a serpent lying under
a tree and put them in its mouth? You are a fool begotten by
a fool!' Then he checked himself. 'But did you not make an
agreement with the serpent? Breaking one's word means
breaking one's faith. What will you do?'

'What you will do,' he answered himself, 'is this: don't
return to him at all, and just drive away the camels and other
animals for yourself!'

So this he did, and the agreement with the serpent was not kept.

One day later on, when the drought was still unbroken, some
men came from the sultan to the soothsayer in his home.

'The sultan said that you must come to him quickly!' they
told him.

Frightened, the soothsayer asked himself what the sultan
could be calling him for that day, but he could not refuse the
order, and followed the men. After travelling for some time
they came to the assembly where the sultan was sitting, and
shook hands with him. They sat down and exchanged news,
and when they had finished the sultan said to the soothsayer,
'I have called you about a matter which is always easy for you
and difficult for us.'

'And what is that?' answered the frightened soothsayer.

'Well, it was you who saved us from both this year and the
bad year before that. All the other people have been destroyed,
first by the war and then by this drought, against which no one
had warned them. As for us, neither men nor animals have
perished, thanks to you and to God. And today we want you to
tell us about the time which is coming!'

'To tell you . . .?' Repeating the sultan's words, the sooth-sayer in his dismay flung himself up and then fell heavily on the ground in a faint. The sultan was seized with fury and moved towards him with a whip: 'Whenever I give that man an order,' he said, 'he is angry and resentful!' But the bystanders took the whip from him, and as he turned away, he said, 'Tell that scoundrel, when he wakes up, that if he does not give me an answer in three days, this sword of mine will kill him!'

When the soothsayer recovered consciousness, the people who were standing over him told him what the sultan had said, and he became aware of the seriousness of his situation. 'You have not the audacity,' he said to himself, 'to go back to the serpent, yet if you do not answer the question which you were asked, you will be killed. What will you do? If you return to the serpent, what will he say to you? Yet whatever he may say to you, have you any better plan? Well, then, simply go to him!' And he left the place and ran to where the serpent was.

'Is it you who comes to me again?' said the serpent, laughing.

'Yes.'

'And what do you want?'

'Today,' answered the soothsayer, 'I was once again asked the same question as before.'

Then the serpent said:

'Tell the sultan who sent you that the sky will bring back the clouds. Tell him that the sky was for a long time barren but that now it will bring back the *Dirir*[1] rains. Tell him that there will be a time when on a night already half spent, the sky will flash with lightning. Tell him that there will be plentiful *Daydo* rains as there used to be. Tell him that the whole country had become dry, but now short rains will pass over it. Tell him that the animals which had suffered much on the long journey to water will find rain. Tell him that the flood water will scurry like a lizard through the valleys bare of vegetation. Tell him that fresh grass will spring up in the bush country round

[1] *Dirir* is the Somali name both of the star Spica and of the rains which in Somali popular weather lore are associated with the occultation of that star by the moon. There are six periods during the year when the likelihood of rain is great, according to this method of weather forecasting, and one of them is called *Daydo*.

the old encampments. Tell him that those animals which have survived will be in milk.

'Tell him that the wives who were banished from the companionship of their husbands during the hard season will make huts as large as stone houses. Tell him that they will put away their old and workaday clothes. Tell him that they will dress themselves in the silk that had been rolled up and stored. Tell him that they will bring out incense burners from nooks and crannies between the mats. Tell him that they will spread sleeping-mats in a snug recess of the hut. Tell him that the husbands who had no thought for love in the hard season will now enter the huts, their bodies less lean. Tell him that now, no longer driven by hunger, they will eat what they choose. Tell him that they will be invited again and again, with tender little words, to take more food. Tell him that their wives will come and go, fetching vessels and utensils. Tell him that as the wives pass to and fro close to their husbands, the love which had grown old will become young again. Tell him that in their revelry and play they will conceive sons of blessing, bright as thunderbolts.

'Tell him that the unmarried men will wed, in a befitting way, the girls of their choice. Then they will be honoured and entertained by riding displays and dancing, and a man who so wishes will turn his mind to faith and prayer.'

The soothsayer went in haste to the sultan, and he was received even more joyfully than before.

A little while later, the clouds rose up one evening far away in the east. 'In truth,' the people said, 'clouds have gathered there!' It was thought that they were small and not the ones which bring rain, but unexpectedly, when the animals came home in the evening, there was lightning in the distant eastern sky. Everyone rejoiced, there were ululating cries of jubilation from the women, and anxiety fled from the hearts of all the people, as was God's will. As they were watching, and in truth not yet expecting anything to happen, suddenly someone said, 'By my virility and my wealth, there are clouds over us! Dig draining ditches round the huts, and put all the weak animals in their shelters!'

This was done, and when the ditches were dug and the animals were well taken care of, the people went to sleep. When a quarter of the night had passed, there was a little rain which just covered the ground and then stopped. The animals were driven out near the enclosure, so that they could drink the water lying on the ground, and the people also collected some. Then at dawn the rain came, lasting until mid-morning, and the animals were driven out to graze. After this the rain did not stop for four days, and the camels, sheep, and goats had their fill of water, while the people had their fill of milk from the animals which had formerly been dry.

Towards the middle of spring, the sultan called an assembly of the tribe and settled all the matters which had arisen during the drought. He then earnestly admonished the people and reconciled all those who had disputes with each other, and finally he called the soothsayer and gave him many animals of every kind.

'By God,' the soothsayer said to himself, 'the serpent saved you from disaster three times, and each time you broke the pledge you gave him. Do not break it this time! Pay your debt of gratitude and take all the animals to him.'

So driving all his animals together he took them to the serpent. 'O serpent,' he said, 'I want to talk to you about three matters. The first one is this: you helped me very much, and I repaid you with evil each time. Now I am repentant and all the things which I received today are here. Take them and forgive me! The second matter is that I want us to become friends. And the third matter is this: you, brother, are a wise man. Tell me about the world and about life!'

'First of all,' answered the serpent, 'as for friendship, I become a friend to no one; I either harm or help a man, according to the purpose for which I am sent. As for repentance and these animals which you have brought me, I have forgiven you, and you can take them back. I return them to you, but I consider the gift as accepted.

'As for the world and life, this I will say to you: world there is but no life. What one calls life follows the world itself. God created the world; then he made many patterns for it and these patterns of the world rule the people. When the time is a time of war, each man, wherever he may be, is an enemy of all others.

Thus it was, during the recent war, that you took up your sword against me, after I had helped you, saying to yourself: 'Cut off his head!' When the time is a time of drought, no man is generous to his fellows, and then it was that you ran away with the animals. When there is prosperity, you will not find anyone niggardly or full of hate, and then it was that you brought all the things that had been given to you.

'Every time, you did what the circumstances forced you to. Now, finally, I shall tell you about myself: I am not a serpent, I am Fate. You will not see me after this day—farewell!'

WEST AFRICA

39

The Pineapple Child

From 'A Gã folk tale', J. Berry, *BSOAS*, xii/2, 1948.

This tale was collected in the field from an exceptionally gifted reciter and represents a good example of one of the most widespread themes in West Africa.

ONCE upon a time there lived a man and his wife who had long wanted a child but did not get one. So they went to an old woman and asked her to help them. The old woman told the wife, 'Go down the road which is straight to your front and when you have gone some distance you will come to a fork. Take the left turning and you will at last see a plantation full of pineapples. One of these pineapples will say "Pluck me, pluck me" :do not pluck it, pluck rather the one which says, "Don't pluck me, don't pluck me." Take it home and hide it behind your water pot. In three days' time you will hear "mama, mama" and you will see a child crying behind the water pot. Take it for your own.'

The wife did exactly as the old woman had told her. When the third day came, she heard the child's crying behind the water pot and when she went to look, she saw a beautiful baby hiding there. She took it up in her arms. Both she and her husband doted on the child and they reared it carefully until such time as it could walk and talk and could be safely trusted.

One day, the father and mother and a girl who lived with them set out for the farm, leaving the child at home, sitting in a bath of water, playing with a gourd which they had made for it. Their intention was that the girl should fetch firewood and return home immediately to look after the child. The child, meanwhile, having played for some time with the gourd, polished it nicely and put it away on some firewood which someone had gathered into a heap.

Not long afterwards the girl came back from the farm carrying on her head a bundle of firewood. She was completely tired out by the work, so much so that she didn't look at the heap of firewood, but crash! she threw down her load on top of the child's gourd and broke it into little pieces. When the child saw what had happened it burst into tears. By the way, the girl's name was Adene—and she turned to the child and said, 'What are you making such a fuss about? What is the matter with you? Are pineapple children always so fussy?' The child was very hurt that Adene should speak like that to it and it began to sing this song and set out to look for its father and mother.

> 'Adene was carrying a bundle of firewood,
> Adene let it fall on my gourd,
> Adene said, "You can tell if you want to",
> Adene said I wasn't a man's child,
> Adene said I was a pineapple child,
> So I'm going to pineapple country, Adene,
> Adene, ooh, Adene.'

About this time the father and mother had left the farm and were on their way home. They heard the song, stopped, stood, and listened to it for some time. Then they realized that it was the voice of their own child that they could hear and the father began to run as fast as his legs could carry him towards the place from where the song was coming. As he ran he could hear the song more clearly and could make out the words. And, by the way, they had already entered the house and had asked Adene what was the matter, and she had told them that (it was nothing), that the child had only gone out of the gate. From what he had heard of the song the man realized that Adene had offended his child and that was why it was running away. And now, he could make out the child's back as it was going off into the distance. When the child saw its father running, it too began to run, and it reached the pineapple plantation just as its father was on the point of catching it. Its father stretched out his hand to grab it, but he could not reach it properly. He did, however, grasp its hair just as it got to its old place; some was left in his hand and he clutched it to his breast.

'That is why it is the man who has hair on his chest.'

'If I get one I will stick it behind your ear.'

40

Oratory of the Chief's Spokesman

These short extracts were translated by Professor J. Berry from
Zimmerman's *A Grammatical Sketch of the Akra or Gã Language*,
Stuttgart, 1854.

The importance of the chief's spokesman or 'linguist', as they were
often known, has been stressed by many but investigated in detail by
none. The stylized language of Gã and Ashanti orators merits study
by specialists before the art is lost, or at least undermined by the
written word.

SPEECH BY BADU ASONKO, SPOKESMAN OF O.S.U.

On the occasion of the imposition of tax: 14 January 1854

LISTEN to what the seven and seven times seven said: They
said 'It is nothing'. But these men are their masters and the
things they tell them are not pleasant. What then? If now, for
example, your wife wrongs you and you say 'I will take her to
the castle and have my master punish her for me,' when you
go, she is snatched from you. If you say 'I will go and bathe in
the sea,' when you go, at once you are caught and punished.
And now they say 'On top of all this a poll-tax is to be levied.'
And there are some of us who have sold their children and
possessions because of a poll-tax like this before, and today
they say—after a long time—it shall be levied again—But
this tax is not going to be paid, heh, this tax is not going to be
paid. Fathers, is this not what you said? [and the answer of all
was] 'Aye, not one penny.'

THE SPEECH OF THE 'LINGUIST' OF DUTCH AKRA IN REPLY TO BADU ASONKO

'IF they say they won't pay the tax, that we can understand;
but they said they would no longer serve the English, that is
not right, heh, that is not right. For all who are lying hereabout,
on the day the English bought the fort, did they not eat fetish?

Were they not all then in the fort. Lo, it is today (and not before) that they say they will revolt. That is not pleasing, if they say so, that is not pleasing, heh, that is not pleasing!

'But seek a good word for me ——'.

BADU ASONKO ANSWERS

'WHAT we said about not serving the English longer, that we take back: we will serve them, but the tax we won't pay and the elders will not go into the fort: but if he gives up his demand for the elders then the nation will have rest, but if he says he will not agree, we also cannot help it. Let happiness come.'

41

How the Older Brother saved the Younger Brother from Death

This and the following story were collected and translated from the Bulu by the Rev. A. N. Krug and published with others after his death in 'Bulu Tales', *Journal of American Folk-lore*, vol. 62, 1949.

Bulu is a Bantu language spoken by about 100,000 people in the southern Cameroons.

Krug records that tales were normally recited by people round the fire during the evening, or even by semi-professional reciters who went from place to place, accompanying their recitations with instruments. Krug's collection, however, was elicited from school-boys in a Mission school.

ONCE upon a time there were two men who were born of the same mother. One of them, the younger, left his brother and said, 'I am going to live in a village of my own.' So he went away, and his wife went with him, and they lived together in a small village. Some days he went away into the forest, leaving his wife alone in the village. One day, as he went again to the forest he found there a man, who was digging pitfalls in the forest. The name of that man was Tatemiañg. Then said this man to Tatemiañg, 'What kind of a man is this, who digs pitfalls like these here in the forest? I think I shall wait here and see how this man digs my grave here today.'

Tatemiañg was angry at this saying and replied, 'Why have you come here today to spoil my luck with these pitfalls?' and again he asked him, 'When will you be dying, perhaps I may yet dig your grave for you.' The man answered, 'After two nights I will die.' But Tatemiañg said, 'No, do not trifle with me, but tell me a certain agreement as to the time you will die,' and the man answered, 'Tomorrow.' Tatemiañg said, 'That is all right with me.' After this the two went back to their homes.

When the next morning had dawned the man was sitting there with a look of despair; and his wife asked him, 'Why are you sitting there with such a look of despair?' and he answered, 'I met a man in the forest yesterday, his name is Tatemiañg, and he says he will come here today and dig my grave, and that is the reason I look so sober and downcast.' A little while after Tatemiañg came and he said, 'I have come now', and again he said, 'I have come now to dig your grave, therefore hurry up now and get ready to go with me.'

Then said the wife of the man to Tatemiañg, 'Please wait a few minutes while I get him some food.' The woman ran in haste to the village of his older brother and said to him, 'A man has just come and he is going to kill your brother in our village yonder.' Then said he to the woman, 'You go back, and I will follow you as soon as possible.' He went in haste and killed a goat and cooked it; and he hastened and soon arrived at the village of his brother, and acted as if he were going right through without stopping at all. But Tatemiañg called to him and said, 'Please come here and listen to this palaver we have.' So he entered into the palaver-house and he sat down and he took his bundle of food, with the liver of the goat cooked in it, out of the basket and he called to Tatemiañg, 'Come now and let us eat together.' So they sat down there together and ate, and when they had finished eating the man said, 'Now it is up to you to pay for the meat you have eaten.' Tatemiañg said, 'Please excuse me just a moment while I go and get a drink.' He went out of the palaver-house, and not only crossed the street, but he went by the house and soon was running back to his town. In this way the life of the young man was saved, because his older brother helped him out of the difficulty.

42

The Englishman and his Pet Animals

See introductory note to Text 41.

ONCE upon a time there was an Englishman, and he used to go hunting and shoot game near his home. There came a day that all the game there was finished. So he said, 'Now I perceive that all the game animals in my own home forest are finished; so I think I will go and hunt over in Germany.' He went to tell his father and his mother of his plan, but they objected and said, 'No, you must not go there.' But he was persistant, and again he said, 'I am going.' So they at last reluctantly consented. So he took his gun, and his cartridge box and his travelling bag, and started on the way to Germany.

As he was going along the way he saw a large female chimpanzee, which was carrying its child. When he was just about ready to shoot the mother chimpanzee with his gun, the mother chimpanzee left the young chimp there and ran away into the forest. The young Englishman took the young chimpanzee with him as a tame pet. He went on some distance farther, and he saw a large female gorilla, and it also was carrying its young. When he was getting ready to shoot the mother, it also left its young and ran into the forest. So he took the gorilla as a pet. As he went on still farther he saw a mother leopard with its young, and just when he was ready to shoot the mother leopard, she left the young leopard and ran into the forest. So the Englishman took the young leopard also as a pet with him. Thus he had three pet animals, a chimpanzee, a gorilla, and a leopard.

At last he arrived at his destination. He told the people there, 'I have come here to find a woman to marry,' and they said to him, 'There is a woman in yonder house you may marry.' So he first took his three pet animals to a small house near by. After that he went to where the woman was in the house, and told her his errand; and the woman fell in love with him. But the woman also said to him, 'There is only one trouble here, and one evil thing, for I have had many lovers before you came, but there is a large and fierce animal here that kills them.' The Englishman replied, 'I surpass all men in knowing how to shoot animals, so this fierce animal will not do anything to me.' The woman again told him, 'That fierce animal is in the habit of coming at midnight.'

As soon as darkness had come the Englishman made his plans and waited and was on guard for the approach of the animal. When it was just about midnight that fierce animal did come. When the Englishman heard it come, and while it was still some distance away, the Englishman went and found a good place to wait for it. When it came near he shot it with his gun and it died. He ran in haste and cut off its tail and he gave that tail to his pet animals; and they kept the tail safely with them. After this the Englishman went back to his house and laid down to sleep.

When the soldier, who was always guarding this woman, heard the report of the gun, he came and ran swiftly to the place where he heard the gun, and there he found the animal dead. So the soldier made a plan, and said, 'I will go and kill that Englishman, and after that I will marry this woman.' For the father of this girl had said, 'Whoever kills this fierce animal, he will marry my daughter, and he need not give any dowry either.' So the soldier quietly went into the house of the Englishman, and found him asleep and cut off the head of the Englishman. After this the soldier hastened to the father of the girl and told him, 'I have killed the fierce animal which used to kill the young men and lovers of your daughter.' The father of the girl asked him, 'Which part of the body did you shoot at?' and he said, 'I wounded it in the side of the body.' The father said, 'My men will bring in the body in the morning.'

When the day had dawned the three pet animals said; 'Where is our master who brought us here?' So they all three went to the house where their master used to stay. When they came to the house they asked the girl, 'Where is our master?' and the woman said, 'He has been killed, there lies his corpse.' At first the pet animals were in great trouble and perplexity and did not know what to do. But soon the chimpanzee said, 'I can put his head back on his neck,' and the other said, 'Go ahead, and put it on indeed.' And he put the head back on the neck. The gorilla now said, 'I can bring him back to life,' and

the other said, 'Go ahead and do it.' And the gorilla did this.
But still the Englishman was not able to talk. So at last the
leopard said, 'I am able to make a magic charm, so that he will
be able to talk.' They all said, 'Go ahead and do it.' So the
leopard made the magic charm, and right away the Englishman asked them, 'What are you all doing here?' They answered,
'You had been killed, but we have brought you back to life
again.'

After this the Englishman took a bath and put on his best
clothes and went and told the father of the woman, 'I have killed
the fierce animal.' But the father would not believe him, and
said, 'The soldier has come and he told me that he himself
killed it; why do you come here like this and lie to me?' The
Englishman said, 'That is not true, and I will prove to you that
I myself killed the animal.' So the man asked him, 'What part
of the body did you shoot at?' And he replied without hesita-
tion, 'I shot at it as it came toward me, from the front, and hit
it in the face.' The father of the woman had meanwhile sent
his men to bring in the carcass of the animal, and when the
men came with the body, and the man who had the daughter
very carefully looked where the shot had hit it and killed it,
they found that it had been hit in the face just as the Englishman had said. So the father of the girl and all the people agreed
without dissent that the Englishman had killed the animal. So
they gave him the woman in marriage.

Soon after this the Englishman took his wife and his three
pet animals and started on the road back to his home country.
When he arrived at the place where he had caught the young
leopard, he released it, and let it go free; when he came to the
places where he had taken the gorilla and the chimpanzee he
also released them and let them go free. At last he arrived at
home again, and he had the beautiful woman whom he had
married as his wife. As far as we know they lived happily ever
after.

43

Why Tortoise is used in preventing Harm by Evil Spirits

An Igbo folk-story told by C. I. Nwako and translated from
the Igbo by M. M. Green.

The Igbo of eastern Nigeria are great story-tellers and this tradition
has persisted right up to the present time (see Part II, Texts 6, 8,
17–18). Miss Green has discussed the oral literature of the Igbo in
greater detail in her 'The Unwritten Literature of the Igbo-speaking
People of South-Eastern Nigeria', *BSOAS*, xii, 1948.

ONCE upon a time two children went to a place called Ogodo,
to the house of a chief of that place called Okolo ('one who likes
excitement'). He gave them *kola* and asked their names. One
of the children told him that his name was 'Heap of sense.' The
other said that his name was 'Foolish child of a dunce.' The
chief asked 'Heap of sense' what his name meant. He said it
meant that he was very clever and could answer any difficult
question whatever. The chief asked the other the meaning of
his name. He said, 'It means I know nothing at all.' The chief
then gave him a big hen and gave 'Heap of sense' a cock, saying,
'Take these and each of you bring me two eggs tomorrow.'
Then they went home. 'Heap of sense' and Tortoise were old
friends.

As the children got home the hen the chief had given Dunce
laid two eggs but the cock he had given 'Heap of sense' laid
nothing. 'Heap of sense' then went to find his friend and told
him how they had gone to the chief's house and what he had
told them to bring him. Tortoise answered, 'My friend, that is
no problem. Don't go tomorrow but let Dunce go. Go yourself
the following day. When the chief asks you why you didn't come
on the previous day tell him that your father was in labour.'
'Heap of sense' went along in two days' time and the chief asked
him why he had not come the day before. He said, 'Sir, it was
because my father was in labour.' The chief exclaimed and spat
in his face and said, 'Have you ever seen a man in labour?'
'Heap of sense' replied, 'Have you ever known a cock lay eggs?'

The chief saw that 'Heap of sense' was certainly intelligent and said to him, 'You are to come tomorrow and pull up the great tree for me that is in front of my house.' 'Heap of sense' said he would do so and went home. He went and told Tortoise, who said there was nothing to worry about. When he arrived he should say, 'Chief, I beg you to chew this stone which is in front of the compound and spray it out on my chest, to give me strength to pull up the tree at once.' 'Heap of sense' went back and said this to the chief, who scolded him and said, 'Have you ever seen anyone who chewed a stone?' 'Heap of sense' retorted, 'Have you ever seen anyone who pulled up a tree as big as this one with his hands?' The chief considered what to do and then said, 'You are to drink up all the water in the sea tomorrow.' 'Heap of sense' then went home and again told his friend Tortoise, who said, 'That is easy. When you arrive dip one finger into the sea, lick it and tell the chief it is not salt enough and you are not going to eat anything which hasn't got enough salt.' The child went and told the chief this, who said, 'Didn't you know that the sea wasn't salt enough?' 'Heap of sense' replied, 'Have you ever seen anyone who could drink up all the water in the sea?'

The chief was astonished at the child's answers and said to him, 'I wish you to bring me whoever it is that teaches you all these things.' 'Heap of sense' went home and told Tortoise, who agreed to come, thinking that the chief would give him some present. They went to the chief's house, where he gave them *kola*, and picked up Tortoise and put medicine in incisions in his face and said, 'Tortoise, you will always be used to render harmless (cover) evil spirits and to drive away wicked people who trouble us. You will be used in divining and your shell will be used to give sense and intelligence to those who lack them, to make them sensible. Go away now and in the evening we will take you for this work.' As Tortoise was going he said, 'Guardian spirit of the land, let me not be used to obliterate evil spirits.' The medicine the chief had put into the cuts in his face answered him, 'You must be used to obliterate evil spirits.' He went and hid in a ditch, but the chief came and asked about him and the medicine told him that Tortoise was in the ditch. The chief said to the medicine, 'Bring Tortoise to me.' The medicine lifted Tortoise out of the ditch. Tortoise was used to obstruct evil spirits and wicked people in that chief's land.

Since that time, therefore, Tortoise is always used in divining, and in giving stupid people some sense. He is also used in covering up bad medicine in Igbo land, and in seizing evil spirits and bad people if they give trouble.

44

Adamu and his Beautiful Wife

A Hausa story, recollected and translated by Bashir Sambo, formerly a student at the School of Oriental and African Studies, London.

It is probably true to say that Hausa occupies a position in West Africa analogous to that of Swahili in East Africa: both languages being spoken by many as a second language, and both having been influenced, in different ways, by Arabic and Islam. While Arabic was the language adopted for recording much of Hausa history, in the East it was only the Arabic script that the Swahili poets used.

The story of 'Adamu' was related to Mr. Sambo as a small child by his parents. The name Sonkowa means 'Desired by all' while Danisa simply means a 'Distant place'.

In a certain town there lived an ascetic whose name was Adamu. Adamu was a man of exemplary character. He was so good that he possessed supernatural power. He could understand the languages of the animals, birds, insects, trees, and stones.

In the same town there was born a beautiful girl who was a few years younger than Adamu. He parents belonged to the middle class. This girl was so beautiful that she was loved and desired by anyone who saw her. The ruler of the town began to court her with confidence that it was he and he alone that could marry such a beautiful girl. Although parents had full control and could control the destiny of their sons and daughters, the parents of that girl could not exercise such control over their daughter. Naturally they gave consideration to any of those important and rich people who were asking the hand of their daughter in marriage including the ruler of the town. The girl chose no one among her admirers but Adamu, the ascetic. The parents did not like to marry their daughter to Adamu because he was a poor man. Though they gave no consideration to anyone but the ruler, yet they were considering him under threat and compulsion. For they preferred marrying their daughter to a rich man, rather than either the ruler or the poor ascetic Adamu.

The girl was determined by all means to marry no one but Adamu. When her parents wanted to compel her to marry the ruler, in order to escape his threat, she stopped eating and drinking and preferred death to marrying anyone but her beloved Adamu, the ascetic. When the parents saw that they were going to lose her they explained the situation to the ruler. They begged him to allow their daughter to marry Adamu so that she might survive. They proposed a plan to him, suggesting that the ruler plan to kill Adamu after the marriage accidentally. The ruler accepted their proposition and allowed the girl to marry Adamu. When the girl heard that she could now marry Adamu, she began to eat again and soon regained her beauty. In the meantime the parents began to think of how to get rid of the ruler after the ruler had got rid of Adamu.

The girl, who was nicknamed 'Sonkowa', was married to Adamu. Both Adamu and Sonkowa were very happy together. Adamu then learned of the plan to kill him made by the ruler and the parents of his wife. He did so through his supernatural powers. When he learned this, he planned secretly to emigrate from the town with his wife.

It was at dawn on a certain day that Adamu and Sonkowa left the town without knowing exactly where they were going. When Adamu and his wife left the town, all the buildings, trees, and occupants of the town were crying and weeping in a language only he could understand. They did so because they knew that if Adamu went away, they would miss him bitterly.

As they left the town, they met a group of ants. The leader of the ants said to Adamu, 'Where are you going to at this time of the day?' Adamu said, 'My wife and I are leaving the town because the ruler is after my life, so we wish to go somewhere where we can live in peace.' The ant said, 'If you leave the town, we shall always be unhappy. Can we join you?' Adamu said, 'I am not leaving the town because I like doing so, but I am leaving because I am compelled to. If you like to join us, you can do so with pleasure.' So the ants joined Adamu and Sonkowa on their way to an unknown destination. As they advanced a little they met Slipperiness and Stumbling. Both asked Adamu for permission to join him. Adamu agreed. No sooner had they walked a little farther than they were met by two crown birds. They too joined Adamu's company with pleasure. Then came a frog and a snake and they both joined Adamu's company. Adamu, his wife Sonkowa, and their friends travelled day and night for many days before arriving at a big town which was surrounded by a high wall which had only one gate. They were all glad to arrive at a town at last. The name of the town was Danisa.

Danisa was a very, very big town. It was so big and so beautiful that it looked more than a town. It was a grand city. The king of that city was a very famous man and he was notorious for his love of beautiful women. The king was a very wise man and a very good and shrewd administrator. He had his police and bodyguard. He had detectives and spies. The chief of spies was a leper whom he chose because no one would dream of a leper being a spy. The office of the leper was at the gate of the town. He was always present at the gate. He left it only when it was closed. There was nothing that could go either in or out of the city without his knowledge. He was so capable in his work that the king had every confidence in him.

When Adamu, his wife Sonkowa, and their company arrived at the gate, the leper saw them and was perplexed by the beauty of Sonkowa. He could not believe his eyes and he was not sure if she was human or an angel. When Adamu saw the leper he understood his train of thought by his supernatural power. He said to himself, 'It looks as if I have jumped from the frying-pan into the fire.' When Adamu and company entered the city, he looked for accommodation and was lucky to find an abandoned old house.

When Adamu reached the house with his company, Slipperiness and Stumbling told Adamu that they would stay in front of the door of the hall of the house. Adamu made a hole for the snake, a small pond for the frog, and several small holes for the ants. The crown birds took the big tree in the house as their residence.

For the first time in his life the leper left the gate while still open in order to follow Adamu and see where he was going to live. As soon as he saw the house of Adamu, he ran to the palace and asked to see the king alone. He told him that he had brought him excellent news. He said to the king, 'Your Majesty, how many ears have you?' The king said, 'Naturally I have two ears, why?' The leper said, 'Add a third ear to your two ears even if it be an imaginary one, for the news is so enchanting that two ears are not enough to listen to it properly.' The king said, 'How can I add what God has not given me?' The leper insisted that the king should add the third ear, even if only an imaginary one. The king agreed and said, 'I have three ears.' The leper said, 'Your Majesty, today I have witnessed a beauty beyond expression. We have a stranger who has an angelic wife who matches no one on earth but you. She is so beautiful that you can never believe your eyes when you see her. If it is the last thing I do, I wish to see that delicate angel become your wife.' The king said to the leper, 'You have said that she is a wife, how can she be my wife then?' The leper said, 'Your Majesty, nothing on earth is beyond your reach. Anything in this city is yours. It will be a misuse of nature if such a beautiful angel is allowed to remain in the hands of such a poor man. You can call him and tell him that you love his wife. I am sure that he will be happy to do what your Majesty wishes.' The king said, 'I do not like to take his wife away from him by force. You should do something to persuade him to give me his wife. I leave everything to you and I shall be grateful if you succeed in making her my wife. Your position will be upgraded as a reward.'

Now that the leper was charged with the responsibility of taking away Sonkowa from Adamu, he began to think what trick he could use. He finally made up his mind to poison Adamu. He therefore put poison in some food. It could kill only male persons. He sent the food to Adamu. When the messenger reached the front of Adamu's house, Slipperiness made the feet of the messenger slip and then Stumbling made him stumble. He fell down on the ground and scattered the food on the ground. Another messenger was sent, he met the same fate. This was done several times without success. The leper at last gave up trying to poison Adamu.

The leper suggested another trick to the king. He asked the king to call Adamu and make him do an impossible thing, telling him that failure to do so would mean losing his wife. Adamu was called by the king. He was given two sacks, one of millet and one of corn. The two contents of the sacks were mixed together and Adamu was told to bring the two grains separate within two days or else he would lose his wife. Adamu took the grains and went away weeping. He came to his house and told his wife of the situation. They both wept. When the ants heard them weeping, their leader came and asked them what was the matter. Adamu explained to them and the ants told them not to worry for God would help them. The ants took the grains, corn and millet, and within a day they had separated them into two sacks—one of corn and one of millet as requested by the king. Adamu went and informed the king that his order was carried out and that the grains were separated in a shorter time than the king had ordered. Both the king and the leper were surprised by the work of Adamu. Adamu was allowed to go. The king then asked the leper what would be done next. The leper suggested that the king's ring should be thrown into the middle of the city's big lake and that Adamu should be told to recover it within three days.

The king sent for Adamu in whose presence the king's ring was thrown into the middle of the city's largest lake. Adamu was told to recover that ring from the lake within three days or else he would have to surrender his wife. Adamu heard the king's order and he went back home weeping and wondering what to do. For everybody knew that it was impossible for any human being to swim on the surface of the lake, even more so to dive in it as the lake was full of hungry crocodiles and water poisonous to human beings. When Adamu reached home he explained the situation to his wife. They sat down weeping and wondering what on earth to do. When the frog heard them, he came and asked Adamu what was wrong. Adamu told the frog what the king had ordered him to do within three days. The frog told Adamu not to worry at all because God was on his side. The frog went to the lake and dived into it. Although he was a frog like other frogs in the lake, he had to fight his way through crocodiles, fish, and other frogs in order to look for the ring. He managed with the greatest difficulty to reach the middle of the lake, but could not find the ring. He could not find it because the largest and most senior crocodile had swallowed it as it was thrown into the lake. He almost lost hope when an idea came into his mind that he should provoke the crocodile to anger so that he might swallow him also. The frog preferred death to returning to Adamu a failure. The frog provoked the crocodile, who became infuriated and swallowed him. The senior crocodile was so large that his belly was like a huge room. When the frog reached the intestine of the crocodile he found the ring together with many other living things which had been swallowed earlier by the crocodile. When the frog found the ring, he began to think of how he could get out of the belly of the crocodile. He got the idea of biting the crocodile and so bit the liver of the crocodile. The biting hurt the crocodile so much that he vomited almost all that was in his stomach. The frog was one of the things vomited. The frog ran quickly to Adamu and took the ring to him. The frog explained to Adamu all the difficulties that he had encountered in getting the ring out of the lake. Adamu was very grateful to God and the frog.

It was now the second day after the order of the king to Adamu had been issued. Adamu went to the palace and took the ring to the king. The king and the leper were more than surprised to see the ring recovered from the lake. The king began to fear that perhaps Adamu and his wife were not human beings. So the king suggested to the leper that he should leave Adamu and his wife alone. But the leper thought that his failure to defeat Adamu and get his wife for the king might undermine his position in the palace, so he did not give up. He started to contemplate the most impossible thing Adamu might be ordered to do. He at last formed the idea of asking Adamu to produce seven new stalks of millet within one month. At this time, it was the winter season. It was impossible to get new stalks of millet in that country or anywhere near. The land was dry and the farmers expected to have rain in order to grow their seeds within the next four months from the time when Adamu was to be asked to produce the seven stalks of millet within one month. When the king heard that idea, he too thought that Adamu would be defeated this time because it looked impossible for anyone to produce seven new stalks of millet within one month from that time. So the king gave his approval to this idea.

The king sent for Adamu and told him to produce seven new stalks of millet within one month or else divorce his wife so that the king might marry her. When Adamu heard the king's order he was very much perturbed for he knew that no miracle on earth could produce new stalks of millet within one month or even within six months at that time of the year. He went home unhappy as before. He informed his wife of the king's order. Sonkowa was very sad because she realized that she was the source of all the trouble to Adamu. They began to weep and yell as before. When the crown birds heard them yelling and weeping they came to them to see what was wrong. Adamu then explained everything to the crown birds. The crown birds asked them to stop weeping. They promised to do all they could to produce the required seven new stalks within the fixed time.

The crown birds then got ready to leave the city in order to fly to the country where they could get new stalks of millet. They bade farewell to Adamu and Sonkowa and went on their way towards the East. As they began to fly, they started to sing the following verses:

> To be or not to be is the will of God,
> To make impossible be possible is the will of God,
> To rain or not to rain, new stalk is of God,
> To find seven new stalks is simple for God
> To possess good faith is to submit to the will of God.

The crown birds continued to fly day and night singing their songs until they reached a place where it was the rainy season and the people had started to sow their seeds. They went on and on and within seven days they reached a place where millet was ripe for the harvest. When they reached a certain farm where the young farmers were harvesting their millet, they stopped at a small stream. They drank water. After they had drunk water, they were transformed into two beautiful girls. They walked and passed by the young farmers. When the young farmers saw how beautiful they were, they were attracted by them. The younger farmers approached them and asked them where they were going in the hot sun. The girls answered that they were visiting some relatives of theirs and that they would soon get back. The young farmers offered to escort them but the girls asked them not to bother because they would get back anyway. So the girls went away as if they were going to a definite place. They went away and stayed for some time and then came back. They found the younger farmers still busy with harvesting their millet. The young farmers invited the young, beautiful girls to rest a little in their farm-hut. They sat there and conversed with one another. The farmers asked the girls where they came from. The girls told them lies as they were not human beings but crown birds. After they had finished their conversation, the young girls said that they would like to start moving towards home. The farmers promised to visit them in their homes. The farmers made two bundles of millet for the two girls and carried them while escorting them. They escorted them a long distance and when the girls saw that they were near the small stream at which they had changed into human beings, they asked the farmers to go back from there and they thanked them very much for their kindness. The farmers made an appointment to visit the girls after two days. The farmers returned to their farms astonished by the beauty of the two girls. The girls walked a little farther until they reached the small stream. It was there that they changed into crown birds. Each of them carried fourteen stalks of millet in their wings. They began to fly home singing as before. They arrived back home within seven days. Altogether they spent fourteen days to and fro. They brought the new stalks of millet to Adamu, who was so delighted that he fainted. He was ordered to produce seven new stalks of millet within one month but within fourteen days he had twenty-eight new stalks of millet. So Adamu took a bath and went to the king with fourteen new stalks of millet. He said to the king, 'Your Majesty, your order has been carried out. I have brought with me fourteen new stalks of millet within fourteen days and not seven within one month as you had ordered me to do. I have brought an additional seven stalks so that you may give them to some of your noble ones. May God save your Majesty. I wish to retire now after carrying out your order.' The king and the leper were very much astonished. The king told Adamu to go away in peace. He further told the leper that he should not have any further new ideas. He blamed the leper very much for making Adamu humiliate him (the king). The leper observed that the king was very angry with him. He did not say anything to the king but left.

The leper went home and began to think of what to do. An idea came to him that he should cause the execution of Adamu.

Now, in that city the penalty for stealing is death. The death-penalty for stealing was started at the time when the thieves disturbed the people of the city. From then on the penalty continued to stand and anyone who stole was executed. So the leper conspired with the lady of the king's chamber, who stole some properties of the king, and with the police, who threw the property into Adamu's house. When the king realized his property was missing, he ordered a search in the houses of the city. The police, who conspired with the leper, went straight to Adamu's house. They searched the house and found the missing property. Adamu was arrested and taken to prison. The verdict was the death-penalty, especially as the property was the king's. The king did not know that this had happened through the conspiracy of the leper, the king's chamber lady, and some of the police. He was in any case pleased that this time he had the means of getting rid of Adamu in order to marry his beautiful wife. The leper, in order to raise his dignity once more with the king, told the king that it was through his idea that this happened. Although the king was not pleased to hear that Adamu was to be executed through a conspiracy, there was nothing he could do, as he wanted very much to have Adamu's wife as his own and this was the only opportunity of getting Adamu out of the way.

Previous to the arrest of Adamu, the snake which Adamu took to the city told him that he would be arrested and that an attempt at his life would be made. The snake told Adamu that when the execution was about to take place he would come and bite the prince, the eldest son of the king, that the prince would faint, and that the only medicine to get the prince to recover would be to rub the liver of a leper on to the bite.

So the king ordered an announcement to be made of the execution of Adamu, the thief of the property of the king. When the day of the execution came, almost all the people of the city were present to witness the execution of the man who dared to steal the property of the king. The wife of Adamu was brought to the place of execution so that as soon as it took place, the king might take Sonkowa, who was to be his wife. The leper regarded the day of execution as a red-letter day for him. He had been waiting for that day for so long because of a number of set-backs. At the place of execution all the nobles of the city were present. Chairs were arranged and the king and the prince, the king's cabinet set in the middle. They all sat down in an air of festivity and then the hour of the execution arrived. As the king ordered the execution to proceed, there appeared a large serpent in the middle of the arena. The serpent went straight and bit the prince and disappeared. The prince fainted. All attention was now given to the prince. All the doctors and learned men tried all they could to save his life but they failed. Whenever one doctor after another gave his medicine the condition of the prince, far from improving, became worse. When all the doctors gave up hope, Adamu, who was about to be executed, asked to be allowed to give his medicine. The leper intervened and condemned any suggestion that Adamu might give regarding medicine for the prince. But the king allowed Adamu to give the medicine. Adamu said that the medicine he had was simple and that was that the liver of a leper should be rubbed on the bite. There was no leper present except the leper who was the chief detective of the king and who had all the time been planning to take away Adamu's wife for the king and through whose conspiracy his very execution was about to take place. The king, realizing that his son was far dearer to him than the leper, ordered that the leper should be slaughtered, that his liver might be used to make his son recover. The leper started to run, saying that there was a leper near by and that it would be unfair for the king to slaughter him. The leper was caught and slaughtered. The liver was rubbed on the bite and the prince recovered and asked the people what was happening. It looked to him as if he had been dreaming.

The king was very grateful to Adamu. He released him and he was very pleased to let him go free. Furthermore, the king invited Adamu to be his grand vizier. Adamu did not accept that offer because he believed in being an ascetic. He felt that he could not combine the post of grand vizier and the state of being an ascetic. So the king gave Adamu and his wife a new house and promised to provide them with food throughout the rest of their lives. He accepted a post of legal and moral adviser to the king.

Though Adamu and Sonkowa were now free to live peacefully, he still continued to live with his sincere friends who had helped him throughout his struggle against the intrigues of the leper. He also sent for the parents of his wife and also his own parents. They all came and they lived happily together. He had several sons and daughters, who grew up and helped in raising the standard of education of the country.

45

The Two Rogues

Collected and translated from the Hausa by J. W. Court,
Kaduna, Nigeria.

This story reflects the traditional hostility between the states of Katsina and Kano.

A number of features in the story should be noted: the bark of baobab trees in Nigeria is sometimes used for making rough blankets; the bark of the tree, after being pounded and made supple and dyed blue, has the appearance of cloth. The high price (20,000 cowries) offered for the gown gives an idea of the depreciation of currency brought about by the importation by European traders of vast quantities of the shells, said to have been brought from the Maldive Islands.

Blind beggars in Northern Nigeria are always distinguished by their sticks and begging-bowls—generally half a gourd. The donkey is the all-purpose beast of burden in these parts; horses being hardly ever used for this purpose. Hausa graves are shallow, seldom being more than three feet deep.

The phrase 'The rat's tail is off' is the traditional end of a Hausa folk-story.

THIS is the story of two rogues—one from Katsina and the other from Kano. The one from Kano went and cut a strip of bark off a baobab tree and took it along to the dye pit and dyed it blue. Then he went and bought some cones of indigo and after he had moistened the bark with water spurted from his lips, he beat the indigo into the bark to make it darker and finally folded all up in a piece of paper.

The rogue from Katsina meanwhile had got a goatskin bag and having picked out suitable sized pieces of gravel filled it almost to the top. Then he took about 200 cowries and spread them over the gravel at the mouth of the bag. Then, having tied the bag up, he set off, intending to go to market. On the way he met our hero from Kano. 'Hello, friend,' he said, 'Where are you off to?' 'I'm bound for market,' said the other. 'What are you taking to sell?' 'A dark-blue gown,' he said. 'Well met,' said the man from Katsina 'I intended to buy a gown. Here's my money, 20,000 cowries.' 'How fortunate,' said the man from Kano, 'I want to sell a gown and you want to buy one. Give me the money and I'll give you the gown.' 'Agreed,' said the man from Katsina, and gave the man from Kano the money, and took the gown in return. On this they parted and one went one way and the other went another.

As soon as they were out of sight of one another they left the road and ran into the bush. The man from Katsina thought that he had put one over the man from Kano, and the man from Kano thought that he had got the better of the man from Katsina. Then each opened up his prize to see what he had got. 'Well, I never,' said the man from Katsina, 'that fellow from Kano sold me a piece of dyed baobab bark.' Meanwhile the man from Kano had shaken up the goatskin bag and discovered the 200 cowries mixed with the gravel. 'Well I'll be blowed,' he said, 'that chap from Katsina has sold me a pup!'

So they both set off again and it was not long before they met. 'Well,' said the man from Kano, 'you're an artful blighter.' 'So are you,' said the man from Katsina. Then they decided that since they were equals in guile it would be better for them to join forces and set out together to make their fortunes. So they went off, one behind the other, until they came to a town. There they obtained gourd-bottles and begging-bowls and sticks and took to the road again.

They went walking on until they reached a place in the deep bush where some merchants were encamped for the night. They hid until it was dark and then with eyes closed they groped their way to the camp and announced that they were blind men. They sat down with the merchants until they fell asleep. Then the two rogues opened their eyes, quickly carried off each piece of merchandise and hid it at the bottom of a disused well.

When day dawned, the merchants found they had been robbed and began to weep and wail. On this the two bogus blind men asked 'Where are our gourd-bottles? Don't say they have taken those.' The merchants turned on them in anger and said, 'You're a fine pair of blind men. You know perfectly well that we've been cleaned out and yet all you can do is to ask whether we have seen your gourd-bottles. Be off with you.' The merchants went off bewailing their loss, leaving the two bogus blind men groping for their sticks and gourd-bottles. When they had gone the two rogues opened their eyes and went to the disused well where they had hidden their loot. 'You go down,' said the man from Kano. 'No, thank you,' said the other, 'you go down.' 'No!' said the Kano man, 'you go down.' So the man from Katsina went down into the well and tied the bundles of loot one after the other on the end of a rope for the Kano man to pull out of the well. Every time the Kano man drew out a bundle he carried it some distance off and returned with a stone which he put at the mouth of the well.

At length the Kano man said, 'Let me know when there is no loot left so that when you tie yourself to the rope I can pull you out carefully. I shouldn't like you to hurt yourself against the sides of the well.'

When there was no more loot left in the well the Katsina man tied a large skin bag to the end of the rope and crept into it and said, 'Here's a heavy load, I've put the last four bundles in it.' 'All right,' said the Kano man, and pulled out our friend from Katsina, who was hidden in the skin bag and took him and laid him alongside the rest of the loot. Then the Kano man went back to the well and into it dropped the stones he had collected, one after the other.

Meanwhile the man from Katsina had escaped from the bag and was busily engaged in carrying off the bundles of loot. When the well was full of stones, the Kano man went to where he had left the loot and found that it had gone. He said to himself, 'That fellow from Katsina can't have taken it for he's dead under the pile of stone in the well. Whoever it is he'll come running if he hears a donkey braying, for he can't carry off the stuff single-handed.'

So the man from Kano made a circuit and hid in the bushes and began to bray like a donkey, and the Katsina man came out of hiding and called 'Ahai, ahai, kur, kur, kur!' Suddenly he came face to face with our friend from Kano. 'You're an artful blighter, aren't you?' said the man from Kano. 'And so are you,' said the man from Katsina.

Then said the man from Kano, 'All right, say no more,

show me where you've hidden the loot,' and they went and carried it all to the Kano man's house. Then the man from Katsina said, 'I'm going to see how everyone is at home. I shall be away for three months but I'll be back.'

Towards the end of the three months the man from Kano had a grave dug and he went down into it. Branches were placed over the mouth of the grave. On these were put pieces of broken calabash pierced with holes, and earth was piled on top.

When the man from Katsina asked at the Kano man's house, he was told that the Kano man had been dead for the last four days. 'Take me to the grave,' he said, 'so that I can see for myself.' When he got there he said, 'Ah, well, everyone must come to it sooner or later. I would advise you, however, to get some thorns and cover his grave to prevent the hyenas digging it up. If you will put me up tonight, I'll go home tomorrow.'

Back in the house they brought him food to eat, but he wouldn't eat anything because, as he said, his friend had died.

That night the man from Katsina got up and went to the grave. There he began to dig up the earth covering it, grunting like a hyena. On this, the man from Kano, thinking he was about to be eaten by a hyena, began to call for help. 'All right,' said the man from Katsina, 'you can come out.' So the man from Kano came up out of the grave and they went and divided up their wealth. That is all.

The rat's tail is off.

46

Bambara Knights

The Valiant knights Kala N'dji Thieni and Kala N'dji Korobba

A Bambara tale recorded and written in French by Mallam Amadou Hampate Ba and published in *Black Orpheus*, November 1959, in an English translation by Una Maclean.

Bambara is spoken by about a million people in Mali, Upper Volta, and the Ivory Coast.

WHAT I am about to relate, Sine Koumare told me, is a true account of what took place in the land of Kala, which extends between Sokoto and Sansanding, on the left bank of the Niger.

Sassa, Souakou, Sagala, Markadougou, Seribala Tiemedala, &c., are some of the villages in this province celebrated in the history of the Sudan.

It was into Kala country that Toro Koro Mari, the brother of Bna Ali, the Emperor of Segou, retreated to continue the struggle against the Toucouleurs of Ahmadou Cheikou, the King of Segou.

There were in Kala two warriors, two warriors equally brave, brave in every sense of the word. They were generous, utterly without affectations, and always making fun which was never malicious.

In the town they would permit a 'Bilakoro' (an uncircumcised babe) to tweak their ears and even their beards. They would only laugh till they cried, in sheer indulgence. But as soon as the war-drums, the trumpets, and the metal bells shouted their confused alarm and when the powder of the assailants sounded eloquently from afar, they became once more their true selves: fearless knights, invincible warriors, scattering all before them in a great wave which mowed down the grass and everything which ventured to appear above ground.

The elder of these warriors was called Kala N'dji Korobba, that is to say: 'The eldest of Kala', and the younger Kala N'dji Thieni, which is to say: 'The youngest of Kala'.

Kala N'dji Thieni had, for his part, the vigour and fearlessness of youth. He had the ambition of one who believed himself born to conquer all that was most precious and most rare upon the earth. He believed that the turtle dove cooed amongst the branches simply to salute his passage. . . . And that the bugle bird only opened her beak to chant his praises. . . . And that the flowers of the deepest jungle, just as those of the rolling plains, opened their petals only to smile upon him and perfume his path . . . . The local people used to say: Kala N'dji Thieni is so brave that every morning he wakens Death from his bed by pulling his tail!

As for Kala N'dji Korobba, he was a master of arms and a matchless marksman. He was also the calmest man in the whole world, a man whose heart could not be moved!

Kala N'dji Thieni had only to see an opponent to measure himself against him, and Kala N'dji Korobba never measured himself against an opponent without making a corpse of him.

Kala N'dji Thieni pounced upon the enemy with the speed of a falcon dropping on a bird. Thus it often happened that he hurled himself upon some difficult customer who caused him to lose quite a few hairs into the bargain, but without ever succeeding in vanquishing him. As for Kala N'dji Korobba, he was like a lion, trained in the chase. He well knew how to avoid an aggressive leap and how to rebound upon someone wishing to parry his attack. His prudence, however, did not in the least prevent him from being, on the field of battle, a somewhat disdainful 'lion', who is wise enough not to give in to impetuousity.

Kala N'dji Korobba: Sakanapat-ti! (Good God!) He never pointed his gun except to press the trigger and his weapon was never aimed upon someone without spitting out death propelled by a divine fire. The shots fired by Kala N'dji Korobba were invariably applauded by a monstrous echo whose intensity and duration set the monkeys and the squirrels dancing for long afterwards among the tufted tree-tops. If Kala N'dji Korobba saw a man right in front of him he only missed killing him out of pity and also in order that he could put out one of his eyes, thus adding to the number of one-eyed men whom the superstitious try to avoid seeing first thing in the morning when they get out of bed.

But be that as it may, there was no one who did not know him and some even said loudly: 'There is not one in all of Kala who would dare to pit himself against Kala N'dji Korobba, apart only from Kala N'dji Thieni. He is, after all, the only one who is fit to wear the cast-off sandals of Kala N'dji Korobba.'

Such a comparison was not calculated to please Kala N'dji Korobba! And so he said one day in public: 'If the people of Kala continue much longer to compare me with Kala N'dji Thieni, that stripling of Kala, popularly known as "The last born of Kala," I shall turn him front to back and back to front until there is nothing left of him!' But in spite of this declaration, the heart of Kala N'dji Korobba continued to be tormented by the voice of the Tempter, urging him in a whisper to cut off Kala N'dji Thieni in the midst of his days, that little kitten who wanted to play at being a tawny lion.

The friends of Kala N'dji Thieni, having had wind of the

declarations of Kala N'dji Korobba, informed Kala N'dji
Thieni, so that he might know what the heart of the old lion had
in store for him.

Kala N'dji Thieni said to his friends: 'I must thank you for
your warning, but be reassured. Kala N'dji Korobba shall
never have my life! On the contrary, let me assure you that
though the whole world trembles in the presence of Kala N'dji
Korobba, when I am before him I feel myself only in the presence of a hero whose exploits and paths I wish to imitate and
pursue. To be sure, I would be the last to deny that the moustache of Kala N'dji Korobba is bristly and his beard is dense.
But who has been telling you that I shall forever remain
innocent of moustache or beard? Furthermore, I should point
out to Kala N'dji Korobba that he ought never to forget that
the great baobab tree, which even the elephant respects in the
heart of the forest, has sprung from a grain scarcely bigger than
a little bamiko bean.'

Thus defiance was hurled and accepted—in words. Who
would be the first to translate it into action? Kala N'dji Korobba
could not—tradition forbade it—provoke a younger brother.
So he would be obliged to await a propitious moment. And
that moment was not to be long in presenting itself.

There was in Kala a young maiden called Tene Thiegni
(Pretty Monday). She was a childhood friend and, by repute,
the 'Ton-Moussonin' of Kala N'dji Thieni. Each youth selected
for himself a girl whose chosen knight he became. He defended
her upon all occasions. He had prior right to flirt with her and
she was in fact his platonic love or Ton-Moussonin.

Kala N'dji Korobba married Tene Thiegni.

The friends of Kala N'dji Thieni began from that moment
to tease their companion. They composed a dialogue which
two of them would recite together whenever Kala N'dji
Thieni happened to be with them.

And this is how it went:

'Tell me, O Zan, do you by any chance know of a young
maiden by the name of Tene Thiegni?'

'I know her very well indeed, my dear M'pe.'

'Will you kindly describe her to me, then, because I, you
must believe me, I do not know her at all.'

'By all means. Tene Thiegni, as her name suggests, is a

veritable "Pretty Monday". A beauty with firm, round breasts! By Allah, she is beautiful; beautiful in profile, beautiful from the front, beautiful from the back, and beautiful from every angle! A nymph with white teeth like the cowries of the Orient, her lips moulded like those of the fair women of the distant east.'

'And her buttocks?'

'O Zan, the buttocks of Tene Thiegni are the finest in the whole world, and no one could ever succeed in reproducing her curves, for the mould used to make them was brought by spirits from the very dome of the heavens where souls in the moment of incarnation may admire it.'

'O Zan, in the name of Allah, for God's sake, pray tell me about her bearing.'

'The bearing of Tene Thiegni. Such allure, such poise! The graceful movement of her haunches is not even equalled by the languorous female ostrich as she makes her leisurely way to an amorous assignation atop a white sand dune of the Sahara.'

'I have heard it said that Tene Thiegni can wriggle her whole shape superbly too. Is it so?'

'To be sure, it is the sober truth. Let Tene Thiegni but roll her hips before the most faithful of husbands and you will see him make off pell-mell, or rather run, indeed . . . what am I saying . . . gallop off like a colt which has never before felt the saddle.'

'And what would a chief sacrificial priest do before her?'

'If Tene Thiegni, smiling, and especially if accompanying her smile with a come-hither look, said to the sacrificial priest: 'If you want me, take this knife to pieces and give the bits to me,' with his right hand the priest would offer Tene Thiegni the sacred blade whilst with his left hand he gave her the consecrated hilt.'

'Eh! And where actually is Tene Thiegni now?'

'Alas, Tene Thiegni at this moment is to be found upon an iron barque and this heavy vessel floats upon a lake which is of great depth and infested with crocodiles. This lake itself is in the midst of a dense forest which strikes terror even into the heart of Koro Diarra, the grand father lion, King of the Jungle.'

'No one will ever be able to see Tene Thiegni again nor to

chat with her as when, in days gone by, by the light of the moon, she used to dance the Ko Pili with her two long cotton lempe bands trailing behind her as the symbol of her virginity.'

'And how came this change for the worse?'

'Because Kala N'dji Korobba has married her, in accordance with the most rigid rules. He has paid the colas and killed the marriage ox. He has given the portions of sacramental salt. He has performed the traditional ceremonies in her parents' fields. And I can vouch for it that a select procession escorted Tene Thiegni and Kala N'dji Korobba and the latter has known a good fortune which will certainly have the effect of augmenting his courage and prolonging his days. Tene Thiegni will never again be known as the Ton-Moussonin of any man.'

'Who is the one who is lost and "dead" in this story?'

And then all the friends would chant the chorus in unison like this:

'It is Kala N'dji Thieni who is lost and dead. And why? Because he alone had the privilege of frequent *têtes-à-têtes* with her. He was the knight of the fair Tene.'

After which they would all clap their hands, repeating:

'A lost knight, a suitor spurned for ever!'

Kala N'dji Thieni was dying of love. He had always longed to see his friend once more, the damsel he had hoped so fervently to be able to wed but whose hand he was unable to obtain as his first wife on account of the edicts of tradition.

The long separation merely served to reinforce the love of Kala N'dji Thieni for Tene and the mockery of his companions caused him to lose his head completely. He made up his mind to violate the dwelling of him whose very name could put to flight a band of highwaymen and even warriors of great renown.

In the meantime, the troops of Kala were setting out towards the site of an invasion which was taking place against that region.

After a march of ten kilometres the commander of the expedition decided to call a halt and await the evening.

Kala N'dji Thieni set to thinking on the one he loved, the beautiful Tene. Finally he said to himself: 'He who goes to war may return but he may, on the other hand, just as well end his journey in that mysterious country from which no traveller returns. Death is the inevitable end of every living being; I do not regard death as something horrible. But to die without having ever seen Tene Thiegni again without proving to my jealous and teasing friends that I can confront any danger whatsoever for her sake, that indeed would be insupportable.

'In fact,' he concluded, 'I must see Tene again, come what may.'

Kala N'dji Thieni waited for darkness to fall.

The sun kissed the earth, then withdrew his rays, like a weary beast of prey pulling in his claws.

Kala N'dji Thieni's impatience for dusk prevented him from fully appreciating the immensity of the solar disc plunging into the shades of awakening night. When darkness had completely dispelled the light of day and when the hyenas and the lions came out of their dens, and when each thicket took on the aspect of a monster lying in wait, Kala N'dji Thieni decided that the time had come for him to return to the village and see at last, and perhaps for the last time, the beautiful Tene, that young and delicious Bambara damsel with her blue lips painted by an inspired tattoo.

Kala N'dji Thieni arose with the greatest care. Then he sneaked silently out, grabbing his saddle on the way, to remove the fetters from his horse's legs. Silently he saddled the horse and, still without making a sound, mounted and disappeared as stealthily as a thief, into the shadows which were so dense at this phase of the month, into a moonless night with no bright star to illuminate his path.

Kala N'dji Korobba was not asleep. He kept wondering what ever could have made Kala N'dji Thieni set off like that, at one bound. To him it seemed as though this man, so full of the ambition of youth but also possessed by a mad imprudence, must undoubtedly be looking for a way of surprising the enemy and either attacking him single-handed or, at least, being the first to assail him, in the conceited urge to add one pinnacle to the façade of his glory. In Kala N'dji Korobba's eyes such a purpose was a trifle too spectacular. So he said to himself, 'I shall not permit this young fool to commit an irreparable blunder. He is such a rare specimen in Kala that it behoves me to follow him, so then, if he falls into difficulties, he will learn that the lion cub always has need of lessons but above all needs the assistance of the old lion.'

So saying, Kala N'dji Korobba in his turn saddled his mount and, taking with him weapons of defence and of attack, he set out to follow Kala N'dji Thieni, at a respectful distance, so as not [to] be seen.

Such a precaution was quite superfluous, for Kala N'dji Thieni, going at a fast gallop, was not in the least concerned about whom he might encounter. He never once glanced behind him and seemed to disregard all danger which might overtake him from the rear. He hummed a war chant as he rode, interspersed with haunting fragments of songs of ill-starred love.

Imagine the stupefaction of Kala N'dji Korobba when, arriving at the cross-roads, he beheld Kala N'dji Thieni choosing the path which led to the village.

'Where the devil can he be going now?' exclaimed Kala N'dji Korobba. 'Has he perchance omitted to make the propitiatory sacrifice before climbing into the saddle? Has he possibly forgotten to take his most marvellous gris-gris? Can he have been invited to an amorous assignation. . . . All the same, I shall follow him and see with my own eyes,' so Kala N'dji Korobba continued his monologue.

Once arrived in the town the young man did not hesitate or search long for his route. He took the little road which could lead nowhere but to Kala N'dji Korobba's house. When he saw this, the heart of the Red Beast was thrown into terrible confusion, the hair of his head rose up on end and every hair upon his body bristled too. And in the twinkling of an eye, Kala N'dji Korobba had made one thousand and eleven suppositions, some better and some worse than others, and in the words of the proverb dear to Sudanese storytellers, 'the two groups of ideas did battle within the four chambers of the heart of N'dji Korobba'. The worst ones overcame the good and in the end the latter were expelled and blown out through Kala N'dji Korobba's hugely distended nostrils. Kala N'dji Korobba loaded his gun. As he crossed the street he endured every variety of horror, from those which one can fell [*sic*] and tell to those which only the red devil of the baobab tree inflicts upon unfortunates who catch him stealing his mother-in-law's chickens.

Kala N'dji Korobba cursed the day of his birth; likewise he

cursed his eyes and his ears for allowing him to see and hear
what he ought never to have seen or heard.

'Of one thing I am certain,' he said to himself, 'that today
I shall do two irreparable wrongs. I shall kill a man and I shall
dishonour a woman, if my worst fears are realized.'

Convinced that he would learn of his dishonour and that he
would be obliged to do all that was required of a dishonoured
husband, Kala N'dji Korobba bit his lower lip fiercely between
his teeth. He screwed up his countenance, adopting such a
scowling, ferocious glance that anything passing across his field
of vision appeared to him fantastically doubled.

Kala N'dji Thieni indiscreetly fastened his mount to a
stake fixed at the entrance to Kala N'dji Korobba's house and,
without hesitating or waiting in the vestibule, penetrated right
into the inner courtyard. 'Tene Thiegni, Tene Thiegni,' he
cried.

Tene, after a short silence during which she was presumably
putting on her wrapper, replied:

'Who is it?'

'It is I, Kala N'dji Thieni. I have come to see you. If you
can come out it will afford me the greatest pleasure.'

'To see me, at such an hour? You must have come with bad
news, if so, please, I pray you, let me know the worst.'

'No, Tene Thiegni, I am no messenger of misfortune; on
the contrary, I come to say a few private words to you concerning myself alone. I shall have to go back almost at once.'

'I don't care who comes,' Tene declared.

She brought out a Macina mat which she threw on the ground
and placed at each end of it decorated leather cushions which
were stuffed with sweet-smelling herbs. She lit an oil lamp,
took out her basket of cotton, and sat down at one end of the
mat.

Kala N'dji Thieni took his place opposite her. 'Why is it
you have come to see me?' Tene Thiegni asked once more.

'Tene Thiegni. . . . We were childhood friends, weren't we?
I have always held you in respect and defended your honour.
Inviolate I met you and so I shall return you to whom you
belong.'

'You speak truly,' she acknowledged. 'But,' she went on to
say, 'what I cannot understand is why you, who were always

so respectful and correct when I was available and at your mercy, should wait until I am become the sacred property of someone else, and of such a one . . . to come by night, against every rule of Bambara morality and the proprieties of Kala country, to force my door. No, my dear brother Kala N'dji Thieni, make haste to tell that you are come to inform me of my husband's death and that you only wish to prepare me for my misfortune before announcing it. I am deeply touched by your concern but I should prefer to know the whole truth, and the sooner the better.'

'Only God, who created him, can kill your husband,' replied Kala N'dji Thieni. 'He is a warrior. . . .' At this word Kala N'dji Thieni stopped as though pulled up short. . . . He took out his pipe which he proceeded to fill casually, extracted from a little woven cotton purse a flint, an iron all ready, and some tinder. He then selected a morsel of tinder held it near the flint and struck twice upon the middle of the iron. The sparks emitted from the flint set the tinder alight and Kala N'dji Thieni lit his pipe. He inhaled two puffs which he then blew up into the leaves of the porch under which he sat opposite Tene Thiegni. He gave her a long, devouring glance and sighed profoundly.

Kala N'dji Korobba stationed for some time past within the porch, covered the two young people with his rifle, then raised his weapon and still waited, without quite knowing why. Meantime he was listening intently, so that nothing passed between the two lovers—for Tene was the lover of Kala N'dji Thieni —should escape his ear.

Tene went on spinning her cotton, as was the custom, and Kala N'dji Thieni watched without interrupting her.

In the meantime Tene's cat came out of the house. Arching his back he turned round and round his mistress as though placing her at the centre of a charmed magic circle. Presently he went and lay down between Tene Thiegni and Kala N'dji Thieni, right in the middle of the mat.

Tene said to Kala N'dji Thieni: 'I have always heard it said by the servants and slaves that you and my husband are equal. Nevertheless, how actually does my husband bear himself in the wars? I should so much like to hear your appreciation of him.'

'The slaves and the servants of the compound are unmitigated liars. They say just so much as it pleases them to say, but verily they say little of truth. They know the black lie better than the white truth. If you want to know the truth about your husband, know that. . . .' At these words a slight unexpected sound came from amongst the wood and straw of the porch roof. Tene's cat raised his eyes. His gaze caught that of a mouse who was squabbling with some others in the straw. The unfortunate one lost his balance and tumbled down, right between the paws of the cat which straightaway strangled him without the slightest difficulty.

Kala N'dji Thieni said in an urgent tone: 'Tene, did you see how your cat treated the mouse?'

'Yes indeed, I saw it perfectly, and their struggle was brief,' declared Tene.

'Well,' continued Kala N'dji Thieni, 'thus it is that your husband will treat any man who dares to confront him. He is indubitably the most valiant of the children of Kala. He is the model whom we imitate. He has never been known to glare upon a man without causing him to piss with terror.'

'I am proud of my husband and I am also proud of you, who know him so well and are yet prepared in spite of it all to violate his home.'

A moment or two later Tene resumed, saying to Kala N'dji Thieni, 'My brother, so far you still have not told me the reason for your nocturnal visit which is tarnishing the good name of us both and which may open two cold tombs?'

'Very well, Tene, I have come this evening to bid you fare-well. Tomorrow we advance to the attack. When the enemy appears I shall certainly kill many of them but equally, perhaps, I may be killed myself. Yet to die without having heard your silvery laughter, to die without acquiring a store of your gentle words, would be to condemn myself to die daily in that country where there is no death: in the other world.'

So the talk continued, without the two young people betraying by the slightest gesture any intention capable of alarming a husband's heart.

Tene Thiegni, without exciting in her lover even any of those gestures which a well-brought-up young man might show in the presence of an appetizing female, said:

'Are you certain, Kala N'dji Thieni, that you have not come here to possess me?'

'No Tene, I have not come to take you. I still continue and I shall for ever continue to respect the woman whom I have always loved and respected, even when she was at my mercy.'

'You must be truly mad to venture into a house whose proprietor, as you yourself said, can make others piss with terror by his mere glance. You must be well aware that my husband would not hesitate to dispatch you to the other world should he surprise you in his house, beside his wife.'

'Yes, Tene, I know all that and I must confess that, in truth, I am mad. Simply realize that it is in the nature of certain fools to penetrate, at the risk of their lives, into forbidden territories, merely to pause there and admire things which they desire though they may never possess.

'Thus you are for me an inestimable treasure, which it pleases me to gaze upon at the risk of my life, but I shall never steal it. Besides, the purple dawn will before long transform the colours of nature and the gentle night will deprive us of his aid; I must needs go. I do not wish my elder brother Kala N'dji Korobba to be aware of my escapade. He will believe me dead and is capable of scattering many skulls to avenge me.'

At these words Kala N'dji Korobba rapidly rejoined his mount and disappeared.

And a few moments later Kala N'dji Thieni did likewise.

The following morning the two heroes of Kala attacked the enemy. They wounded many, killed many also, and led back a long train of war captives.

Several days after their return from the wars, Kala N'dji Korobba caused a superlative mead brew to be prepared and he invited Kala N'dji Thieni to come and drink with him whilst playing M'Pari. This game, very popular amongst the ancient Sudanese, is played just like chess. Little sticks of wood and straw replace the pawns. The board is supplied by a square traced out upon a patch of sand or dust.

Kala N'dji Korobba invited Tene Thiegni to stay near at hand so as to be able to serve drinks to his guest.

It is the custom, amongst the players at M'Pari, to make certain exclamations. The words pronounced are often in the nature of observations, sometimes purely poetical, sometimes

more or less provocative and often constituting a direct challenge
to a duel which may be confined merely to unkind remarks. It is
not uncommon, however, for the words pronounced during a
game of M'Pari to be settled by recourse to arms.

Tene served the first calabash to the two friends. Kala N'dji
Korobba, after emptying his cup cried, 'Thirst quenching and,
at the same time, obnoxious liquid which can make a man feel
that he speaks with the voice of a king.'

Thus speaking, Kala N'dji Korobba seized between two
fingers of his right hand two wooden sticks and placed them in
one of the positions of the game. Then he said, looking pointedly
at Kala N'dji Thieni, 'Drink, my guest.' Addressing the pieces:
'Be off there, into that hole, to signify to whoever has ears to
hear that several days ago, at Kala, beneath a porch, at an
advanced hour of the night, by the light of a lantern, certain
words were exchanged. If they had not been pronounced Kala
would be now turned upside down. Such fear and turmoil would
reign there that a pregnant camel would be seeking escape
through the eye of a needle.'

After which he added, 'Kala N'dji Thieni, my younger
brother, let us drink! The youth who declines a drink will
never accept a challenge.'

Kala N'dji Thieni understood the allusion full well. He wasted
no time in trying to discover how Kala N'dji Korobba had
learnt of his interview with Tene nor, which was more important, how he had managed to overhear their conversation. He
replied promptly, placing two straws in a chosen hole upon the
board: 'Straws of brisk repartee, plant yourselves there, straight
as a young palm tree whom the impetuous winds cannot bend.
And say, to whoever cares to hear that, if whoever pronounced
those words beneath the porch where he sat by the most beautiful and adorable woman of Kala had suspected his words were
being overheard by another, Kala would now find itself turned
upside down: even if Kala and the whole world with it were so
upset that the Niger returned to its source, the words which then
were offered would never have been spoken.'

Tene said, as she served the second calabash to the two men,
'Is not he who finds a fortune without owner and guards it
intact until the proprietor arrives a man worthy of trust and
admiration?'

'But be that as it may, I declare that a woman who would give herself to any man with whom she spoke or laughed, merely out of courtesy, would be no woman worthy of the name but only like a well at the entrance to a caravanserai, open to the mercy of travellers of all sorts, conditions and castes.'

PRINTED IN GREAT BRITAIN
AT THE UNIVERSITY PRESS, OXFORD
BY VIVIAN RIDLER
PRINTER TO THE UNIVERSITY